IDEAS FOR MATHS PUZZLES

KS1

P1 to 3

AUTHOR
Doreen Lewis

EDITOR
Joel Lane

ASSISTANT EDITOR
Clare Miller

SERIES DESIGNER
Anna Oliwa

DESIGNER
Rachael Hammond

ILLUSTRATIONS
Gill Richardson

COVER ARTWORK
Ian Murray

Text © 1999 Doreen Lewis
© 1999 Scholastic Ltd

Designed using Adobe Pagemaker
Published by Scholastic Ltd, Villiers House, Clarendon
Avenue, Leamington Spa, Warwickshire CV32 5PR

3 4 5 6 7 8 9 0   2 3 4 5 6 7 8

British Library Cataloguing-in-Publication Data
A catalogue record for this book is available from the
British Library.

ISBN 0-439-01676-2

Contents

Introduction

Competence in number is an important life skill. Mathematics is all around us, yet mathematical concepts are often misunderstood. Many adults display a lack of confidence in maths, equating it with 'sums' which have only two possible outcomes: wrong and right!

It is often the unfamiliar language of mathematics that feeds this lack of understanding of its broader connections to everyday life. This problem needs to be tackled at the beginning of the learning process if it is not to become an obstacle to understanding later on. Since pre-school children start by 'playing' their maths experiences and enjoy them without anxiety, similar strategies should be adopted to continue this stress-free approach to learning basic skills.

Puzzles provide children with 'play activities' (physical and mental) which allow them to work out for themselves, with careful guidance, the key elements of problem solving. They can then generalize these insights into broader learning areas. The teacher's job is to provide the appropriate structure and language to assist the children in acquiring these key skills. When using puzzles to teach problem-solving strategies, we are building confidence through 'play' and establishing a firm foundation upon which new skills can be introduced in the future. This is the basis on which the National Numeracy Strategy Framework is defined.

The maths puzzles in this book have been designed to help teachers provide children with problems which they can discuss and think about, thus developing key skills with wider cross-curricular links. Using material that is familiar to children and is easily accessible allows them to engage quickly with the set task. The teacher will find the planning and resources needed outlined clearly in the 'Classroom organization' section of the notes for each activity. The other sections are given as:
- 'Objective' – what it is hoped each child will achieve.
- 'What to do' – a plan for the lesson.
- 'Differentiation' – suggestions for support and extension.
- 'Now or later' – further activities to broaden or consolidate the experience.

Various teaching styles are suggested, including whole class teacher-led discussion and activities as well as children working in groups, with a partner or individually from the photocopiable support material that accompanies some of the puzzles. Since children need opportunities to develop the language of maths and use it fluently to talk about their activities, responding to and asking questions is a crucial element of understanding basic concepts. Teachers need to set a model of good questioning for children to follow. Guidance is provided as to how this can be done – not by scripting 'teacher talk', but by offering suggestions as to how you might introduce and conclude the puzzle activities.

In this way, you will be providing children with a mathematical language with which they can talk to each other about their own experiences. It will also enhance their mathematical reasoning, encouraging them to generalize and make predictions, as well as helping them to recognize patterns and relationships. The children will be encouraged to try different approaches to the same task and be helped to select appropriate materials and methods when faced with mathematical problems – thus extending the boundaries of their understanding of key maths concepts.

Ready To Go: Maths Puzzles aims to ease your planning and make it fully effective. It focuses on problem-solving and mental calculation skills, while incorporating many of the recommendations made for your daily 'Numeracy Hour'. The key objectives that are stated as required in the NSF document have all been covered (see the Skills grid on page 64). These skills are as follows:

Reception
■ Say and use the number names in order in familiar contexts.
■ Count reliably up to 10 everyday objects.
■ Recognize numerals 1 to 9.
■ Use language such as more or less, greater or smaller, heavier or lighter, to compare two numbers or quantities.
■ In practical activities and discussion, begin to use the vocabulary involved in adding and subtracting.
■ Find one more or one less than a number from 1 to 10.
■ Begin to relate addition to combining two number groups of objects, and subtraction to 'taking away'.
■ Talk about, recognize and recreate simple patterns.
■ Use language such as circle or bigger to describe the shape and size of solids and flat shapes.
■ Use everyday words to describe position.
■ Use developing mathematical ideas and methods to solve practical problems.

Year 1
■ Count reliably at least 20 objects.
■ Count reliably on and back in ones from any small number, and in tens from and back to zero.
■ Read, write and order numbers from 0 to at least 20; understand and use the vocabulary of comparing and ordering these numbers.
■ Within the range 0 to 30, say the number that is 1 or 10 more or less than any given number.
■ Understand the operation of addition, and of subtraction (as 'take away' or 'difference'), and use the related vocabulary.
■ Know by heart all pairs of numbers with a total of 10.
■ Use mental strategies to solve simple problems using counting, addition, subtraction, doubling and halving, explaining methods and reasoning orally.
■ Compare two lengths, masses or capacities by direct comparison.
■ Suggest suitable standard or uniform non-standard units and measuring equipment to estimate, then measure, a length, mass or capacity.
■ Use everyday language to describe features of familiar 2-D and 3-D shapes.

Year 2
■ Count, read, write and order whole numbers to at least 100; know what each digit represents (including 0 as a place holder).
■ Describe and extend simple number sequences (including odd/even numbers, counting on or back in ones or tens from any two-digit number, and so on).
■ Understand that subtraction is the inverse of addition; state the subtraction corresponding to a given addition and vice versa.
■ Know by heart all addition and subtraction facts for each number to at least 10.
■ Use knowledge that addition can be done in any order to do mental calculations more efficiently.
■ Understand the operation for multiplication as repeated addition or as describing an array.
■ Know and use halving as the inverse of doubling.
■ Know by heart facts for the 2 and 10 multiplication tables.
■ Estimate, measure and compare lengths, masses and capacities, using standard units; suggest suitable units and equipment for such measurements.
■ Read a simple scale to the nearest labelled division, including using a ruler to draw and measure lines to the nearest centimetre.
■ Use the mathematical names for common 2-D and 3-D shapes; sort shapes and describe some of their features.
■ Use mathematical vocabulary to describe position, direction and movement.
■ Choose and use appropriate operations and efficient calculation strategies to solve problems, explaining how the problem was solved.

The NSF document describes the types and range of activites in detail that children would be expected to cover in Reception, Year 1 and Year 2 level. Each section of this book addresses particular skill areas to develop at one or more levels (see the section introductions). The importance of linking each skill area to children's own experiences is stressed throughout.

Section 1   NUMBERS

This section comprises 11 puzzle activities, 6 of which have a photocopiable activity sheet for children to complete. All of the activities are focused on the Numeracy Strategy Framework's list of key objectives for number and problem solving in Years 1 and 2. Skills covered include:
- Counting, reading and writing numbers.
- Properties of numbers and sequences.
- Place value and ordering 0–20.
- Basic calculations using '+', '–' and ×2, ×5, ×10 as repeated addition (rapid recall and mental).
- Estimating and checking.
- Fractions $\frac{1}{2}$, $\frac{1}{4}$, $\frac{1}{8}$ equivalents.
- Mathematical vocabulary (based on suggestions from NSF supplement).

The mental maths check is aimed at identifying number problem solving strategies which are covered in the activities and stated as:
- Choose and use number operations and mental strategies to solve problems.
- Make decisions on appropriate 4 rules operations to solve word problems.
- Understand one- and two-step operations in number and record.

FINGERPLAY

RESOURCES AND CLASSROOM ORGANIZATION

Draw six double-hand shapes on the board or flip chart, or on a display chart, as in Figure 1. This activity can be repeated every day as a preliminary exercise before written calculation work.

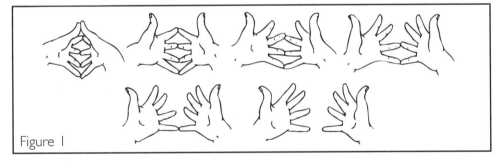

Figure 1

WHAT TO DO

Start by asking the children questions about the usefulness of hands: *What do you do with your hands? Why do you have fingers? Why do you have a thumb?* Encourage them to look carefully at one hand at a time, wiggling the fingers as you indicate them by name: thumb, index finger, middle finger, ring finger, little finger. Count the fingers on each hand together.

Ask the children to imitate you, then place your hands together with the fingers matching (see pictures in Figure 1). Ask: *How many fingers are together?* Pull your thumbs apart, then ask: *How many are still together?* Record the children's responses under the hand pictures. Pull your little fingers apart and repeat the question. The children will be experiencing **even numbers** (from 10 to 2) kinaesthetically. Record the even complements of 10 under the hand pictures: 8 + 2, 6 + 4, 4 + 6, 2 + 8.

Show the children your hands with the open palms face up and fingers folded over them. Raise pairs of fingers to show the even numbers from 2 to 10. Now challenge the children to show you the **odd numbers** 9, 7, 5 and 3, using fingers from both hands. Discuss how the odd number 1 and the number 0 (zero) can be shown: *Can you show me 1 using your two hands? What about 0 – how would you show that?*

OBJECTIVE
To explore:
- number bonds to 10;
- odd and even numbers.

CROSS-CURRICULAR
MUSIC AND ENGLISH
Songs and poems with actions.

DIFFERENTIATION

The children could work in pairs to explore number bonds to 20, using two pairs of hands. Eventually formal sums may be recorded using addition or subtraction problems with gaps to be worked out and filled in. Include sums with 0 and missing '+' or '−' signs.

$$10 - \square = 9 \qquad 1 + \square = 10$$

$$8 + \square = 10 \qquad 10 - \square = 8$$

Figure 2

NOW OR LATER

■ Play this finger game in pairs: one child says a total and holds up part of it, and the other child has to hold up the difference.
■ Find and sing counting songs, or say counting rhymes, using fingers to show the numbers.

NUMBER LINES

OBJECTIVE
To use:
■ a 0–10 number line;
■ the ordinal numbers **first** to **tenth**.

CROSS-CURRICULAR
ENGLISH & MUSIC
Poems and songs.
HISTORY
Number systems.

RESOURCES AND CLASSROOM ORGANIZATION

You will need three sets of large flashcards with the numerals 0–10, the corresponding number names and the ordinal numbers from 1st to 10th. These will be fixed with pegs to a 'washing line' at child height during the lesson.

WHAT TO DO

Ask the children to recite the numbers from 1 to 10. Hold up the numeral flashcards in random order (including the 0 card) for them to identify. Hand out the cards to individual children as they are seated in front of the prepared 'washing line'. Ask all the children to repeat the numbers to 10 slowly in the right order. If nought or zero is not mentioned, ask the children holding numbers whether they all heard their own numbers.

Display the 0 card and say that 0 means *no things or nothing* – so where should it come in counting? Once they have decided, ask all the children with numbers (including 0) to come to the washing line and sort themselves into a correct order; the other children may call out and help if needed. Give each child a peg to hang the number on the line. When they have done this, they can return to their seats. All the class can check the result by reciting the displayed number sequence.

Hold up the number name flashcards in random order; help children to identify them and to exchange each word with the corresponding pegged number. Once the new list is complete, read the number names together. Finally, exchange the number names for ordinal number cards: one for 1st, two for 2nd and so on. This may require some teaching discussion, but will reinforce the numeral recognition and introduce the ordinal feature for later work.

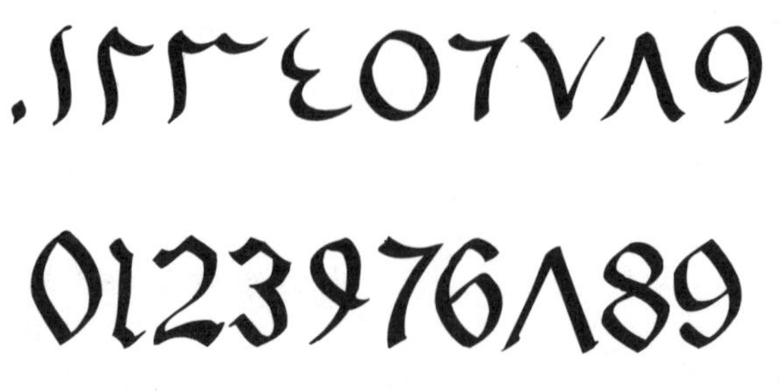

Figure 3

DIFFERENTIATION

The three activities may need to be repeated one at a time, on separate occasions. Some children will be able to predict further odd and even numbers, so that the number line can be extended to 12 and eventually to 20 as competence increases.

NOW OR LATER

■ Explore how numerals are written down in other number systems, such as Roman, Egyptian or Arabic. (See Figure 3.)
■ Find out all you can about the word **zero**.
■ Demonstrate how a number line can be used to count on and backwards, and thus to add and subtract.
■ Use the numeral or number name cards to accompany such songs as 'There Were Ten in the Bed' and 'The Twelve Days of Christmas'.
■ Draw some pinmen in a race on the board. Label the winner and the runners-up using ordinal numbers.

WHERE DO YOU LIVE?

RESOURCES AND CLASSROOM ORGANIZATION

You will need enough large paper house shapes for all the children to put their own house numbers on them. You can adapt this activity to suit the range of numbers the children provide.

WHAT TO DO

Give each child a house shape. Ask them to draw a large door on it, with the number of the house they live in. Any children who live in flats need not be excluded here as they will still have house numbers. A block of flats is a street that goes 'up' rather than 'along'. Start your discussion by asking: *Who has a single number on their door?* Let those children come forward and show their houses to the class. Ask them to arrange their house numbers in order, largest to smallest. They can then return to their seats.

Repeat the process with those children who have a two-digit number on their door. This will mean ordering the numbers 10–99, and may be more challenging. Finally, order the numbers over 100. Now ask the children to identify the smallest and the largest door number in the class. Ask them to draw their house shape three times, making a small row, and then to put their own house number in the middle house. Can they number the houses on each side? Can they identify odd and even house numbers? Can they say how odd and even house numbers are usually arranged in a street?

DIFFERENTIATION

Group the children according to house number – for example, 1–20, over 20 and over 100. Allow each group to prepare an imaginary street, where each child will draw his or her own house according to the two rules *smallest to largest* and *odds and evens on opposite sides*.

NOW OR LATER

■ The children could write their own names and house numbers on envelopes as part of a 'postal delivery' activity. Sort the letters so that the postperson follows a sensible delivery route. This could run from the smallest to the largest number (by a zigzag route) or cover all the odd numbers and then all the even numbers (a loop route). This could usefully be linked to the 'Number lines' activity (page 6).
■ The children could draw their street and mark their own house and other significant buildings, with their numbers.
■ Collect examples of names for houses from the class and elsewhere. The children could think of names for their houses.

OBJECTIVE
To order a set of numbers.

CROSS-CURRICULAR PSHE
Project work on 'Home' and 'Family'.

TALLYING WITH 5S AND 10S

OBJECTIVE
To use tallying to record numerical data.

CROSS-CURRICULAR
SCIENCE
Recording data.

HISTORY
Ancient number systems (for example, Roman).

RESOURCES AND CLASSROOM ORGANIZATION

Draw a diagram to prompt the class on the board or flip chart (see Figure 4). Also, draw some 'tally puzzles' for solving once the idea is established (see Figure 5).

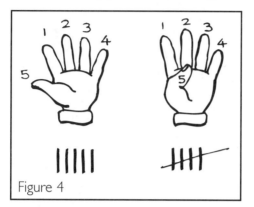

Figure 4

WHAT TO DO

Ask the children to examine their left hand carefully, palm upward. Talk with them about having one thumb and four fingers. (You may wish to name the fingers – see 'Fingerplay' on page 5.) Number the fingers, calling them digits 1, 2, 3, 4 and 5 (the thumb is 5). Ask them to place their 'number 5 digit' across the palm of their hand and look carefully at the result. Now ask: *How many digits can you see?*

The answer, of course, is still five, even in the new formation.

Show the children how to simplify the prepared hand diagram (see Figure 4) into tallying marks to show 5. Explain: *If we repeat this exactly with the right hand, we can tally 10.* Set the children the tally puzzles you have prepared (as in Figure 5). Practise a few together to build confidence.

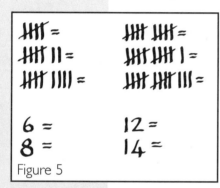

Figure 5

DIFFERENTIATION

■ Work with a group who need support. Keep the tallying easy, always making the finger pattern before recording.
■ For extension, take the numbers to 20 and beyond. Dictate the numbers to be written as tallies.

NOW OR LATER

■ Pairs of children could set each other tally challenges.
■ Ask: *What practical uses does tallying have?*
■ Explore other ways of representing numbers, such as Roman numerals (see also in 'Number lines', page 6).
n Play games of chance with coins or dice and record the results using tallies.

SKITTLE SCORES

OBJECTIVE
To explore a range of number bonds, using the numbers 1–10.

CROSS-CURRICULAR
SCIENCE
Exploring possible outcomes.

PSHE
Life skills such as shopping and game strategies.

RESOURCES AND CLASSROOM ORGANIZATION

Make one copy per child of photocopiable page 16. You may wish to make a larger diagram of the ten skittles on the board or flip chart. A ball and ten skittles may be useful for demonstration.

WHAT TO DO

Ask the children whether they know anything about ten-pin bowling. If necessary, explain the basic idea of scoring by knocking down skittles. You may wish to demonstrate the activity with a ball and ten skittles.

Distribute the photocopiable sheet. Explain that the diagram shows the ten 'pins' (skittles); the children need to write one of the numbers 1–10 on each skittle to play the game and score. The numbers can be written in any order. When the bowling ball hits any skittle, the number on it is scored. The children can make score numbers by choosing skittle combinations to reach a given total. (NB The skittles knocked down each time don't have to be in a straight line – skittles often fall at strange angles.)

It may be useful to point to a diagram on the board or flip chart, choosing two numbered skittles and working out the score, then going on to three skittles as the children's competence grows. The challenge on photocopiable page 16 reverses this process by providing the score followed by 2, 3 or 4 skittle shapes to be filled in with appropriate number bonds. Work through the two examples of a 2-skittle knock-down at the top of the sheet with the class to build confidence. All the possibilities can be written in the box next to the score:
- 6 = 4 + 2 or 5 + 1.
- 10 = 6 + 4 or 7 + 3 or 8 + 2 or 9 + 1.
Note that duplicate numbers (such as 3 + 3) are not possible here.

The children can now complete the three challenges which follow on the sheet. The answers are:
- 7 = 4 + 3 or 5 + 2 or 6 + 1.
- 12 = 9 + 2 + 1 or 8 + 3 + 1 or 6 + 4 + 2 or 5 + 4 + 3.
- 20 = (there are many possible combinations).
You may wish to choose a score (between 10 and 20) and work through all the possibilities with the children. Go on to the final investigation on the sheet: to find the highest and lowest possible scores when knocking down 2, 3 or 4 skittles.

DIFFERENTIATION

- Many more examples of 2-skittle scores may need to be worked through. Help children to explore all of the possibilities if necessary. A standard skittle numbering system (instead of the random one suggested) could be a helpful, stabilizing prompt.
- A full 10-pin knockdown scores 55. Children could work out possible scores for a knockdown of 9, 8, 7 or 6 pins.

NOW OR LATER

- The children could work in pairs to devise a pencil-and-paper skittle game, play it and keep scores.
- Talk about fairground games where 2, 3 or 4 numbers added together win a prize.
- With the children, invent a scoring game for your School Fair.

PINBALL WIZARD

RESOURCES AND CLASSROOM ORGANIZATION

The two sample pinball gameboards on photocopiable page 17 can be used in the two activities suggested here, and in others that you may devise. The sheet should be cut in half, so that you can give the children the correct gameboard for the task you are setting. Make an enlarged version of each gameboard for demonstration.

WHAT TO DO

Game I (see Figure 6) involves addition and subtraction with numbers to 20. Give each child a gameboard. Use the enlarged copy to demonstrate the game plan:
1. Place the numbers 1–9 in the empty circles, randomly (so each child's game may be different).
2. Now follow the zigzag path of the ball from the starting number (10), each time passing through a circle which shows a + or a – sign. Work out each sum as you go, keeping the running score (in the next circle) as you move down towards the final score. A margin is provided for working out the running score.

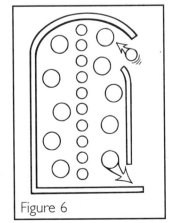

Figure 6

Draw the children's attention to the way the + and – rules alternate. The final scores will also vary due to the random number placement, so the game can be played several times over (using new gameboards).

OBJECTIVES
- Game I: To increase ability to manipulate number addition and subtraction to 20.
- Game 2: To practise forward and backward counting in 10s to/from 100.

CROSS-CURRICULAR PSHE
Confidence building strategies.

Game 2 (see Figure 7) involves forward and backward counting from 10 to 100.
1. Distribute the gameboard. Write 10 in the ball at the bottom and/or 100 in the final score circle at the top before giving out the board.
2. The children must put the other tens numbers (20–90) in the remaining circles. They can work up to 100 or down to 10. They can draw arrows to indicate the ball's route, touching all the numbered circles in the correct order to reach the final score circle (or starting there and going backwards).

DIFFERENTIATION

■ Less confident children could play Game 1 with only the numbers 1–5, changing the starting number to 5 and using only one rule (addition) in any one game. Make a list of multiples of 10, or provide a 100 number square, to help them with Game 2.
■ More confident children could work in pairs to find other ways of counting on or back, using a blank version of the sheet for Game 2. They could also try counting up to or back from 100 in odd or even numbers.

Figure 7

NOW OR LATER

■ With the children, design a similar game that uses a dice to place the numbers.

FUNCTION MACHINES INVESTIGATION

OBJECTIVE

To investigate the possible addition and subtraction number bonds with:
■ odd and even numbers to 9;
■ all the numbers from 10 to 19.

CROSS-CURRICULAR

SCIENCE
Investigation: testing theories and reasoning.

DESIGN TECHNOLOGY
Imaginative interpretation of machines

RESOURCES AND CLASSROOM ORGANIZATION

Each child will need a pencil and paper. Draw three prompt diagrams on the board or flip chart as shown in Figure 8. You may wish to introduce the three function machines one at a time.

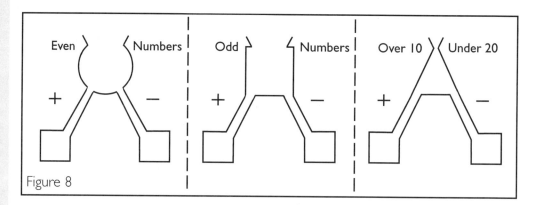

Figure 8

WHAT TO DO

Using the first prompt diagram, introduce the idea by saying: *This is a diagram of a machine that has two functions. One is to add, the other is to take away or subtract.* Point to each function channel and the result box. Continue: *The round machine can only work with even numbers. The square machine can only work with odd numbers.*

Now say: *Let's put an even number, 4, into the round machine. What happens if we use the functions +1 and −1 with the number we have put in the top?* With the children's help, write down the calculations: $4 + 1 = 5$ and $4 - 1 = 3$. Try with the other even numbers below 10: 2, 6 and 8.

Ask: *Suppose we change the functions to +2 and −2? How would that work out? Can you write down all the possibilities yourself?*

This investigation can continue in the same way with the other machines (odd numbers and numbers from 10 to 20). Change the +/− function number to suit the ability of the children. Where negative numbers occur as answers (for example, in the square machine with 1 − 2 = ?), use discussion to introduce the idea of negative numbers to the children.

DIFFERENTIATION
A single machine from Figure 8 could be drawn several times on A4 paper with the same number placed at the top of each machine and the '+' and '−' functions stated, so that each answer can be worked out and written underneath.

   The activity could be extended by using larger numbers or changing the functions to include simple multiplications (such as ×2 or ×5).

NOW OR LATER
■ The children could make card puzzles using different shaped function machines to challenge their friends.
■ A calculator is a more complicated function machine! Explore what it can do.
■ Ask the children to design a machine to do something mechanical, such as making crisps from potatoes.

CATERPILLAR COUNTING

RESOURCES AND CLASSROOM ORGANIZATION
Make copies of photocopiable page 18 as required (see below). You may wish to draw the first example on the board or flip chart.

WHAT TO DO
Look at the first caterpillar on the photocopiable sheet (or draw it on the board or flip chart). Say: *We are going to add 2 to this number and put the answer in this first section. Now we are adding two to **this** number* (indicate the section just filled in). Continue in this way until you reach the tail: *This shows the total of this 2 caterpillar.*

   Work through the other two examples on the photocopiable sheet. All the remaining caterpillars on the sheet have blank heads, so that different numbers can be tried. The pattern sequence is shown in the feet, allowing the cumulative addition total to be written in each segment. The sheet may be photocopied several times to provide a variety of starter numbers below 10; but to begin with, use the number 2 in each caterpillar head.

   The caterpillars will allow you to focus on the following number sequences:
■ a number +1 to +7;
■ an even number +2 to +12;
■ an odd number +1 to +11;
■ the repeating sequences +2/+1 and +3/+2/+1.
You may wish to discuss each sequence, asking: *What can you tell me about this number pattern?* Each cumulative total can be written in the caterpillar's tail. No numbers beyond 50 will be needed.

DIFFERENTIATION
■ The number of caterpillar segments may need to be reduced. Further practice items for the different cumulative addition tasks may be needed.
■ Using a mixture of addition and subtraction sequences will greatly vary the totals and increase the challenge.

NOW OR LATER
■ The children could devise their own sequence code and work out the answers, then give a friend the sequence and challenge him or her to 'crack the code'.
■ Working on squared paper, the children could number the squares 1–20 or 1–50 and colour the cumulative pattern numbers from their caterpillar sequences. What do they notice?

OBJECTIVES
■ To keep track of a cumulative addition total.
■ To recognize simple number patterns.

CROSS-CURRICULAR
TECHNOLOGY
Thinking logically about patterns.

ART
Design repeats.

MULTI-STOREY FLATS

OBJECTIVE
To investigate and draw conclusions from number patterns.

CROSS-CURRICULAR
ENGLISH
- Comprehension skills.
- Following instructions.

RESOURCES AND CLASSROOM ORGANIZATION
Make one copy per child of photocopiable page 19; provide pencils, small cards and a 'postbag'.

WHAT TO DO
Give each child a copy of the worksheet. Say: *We are going to help the postman sort out the letters he has to deliver to these flats. The flat numbers in each block are arranged differently. Under each block, it tells you how to number the flats. Once you've put one number in each window you can answer the questions about each block. This will help the postman to do his job.* Depending on the reading ability of the children, you may need to read out the instructions and questions under each block.

Conclude with a discussion in which the questions for each block are asked, so that the children can volunteer their own answers and explain their reasoning. Block A has 20 flats on 7 floors (the bottom floor has 2 flats, the others have 3 flats) with 6 flights of stairs; Block B has 24 flats on 8 floors with 7 flights; Block C has 24 flats on 6 floors with 5 flights. For Blocks B and C, the children should have alternated rows of odd and even numbers – in Block B, this will be 1, 3, 5, then 2, 4, 6, then 7, 9, 11, then 8, 10, 12 and so on.

Blocks B and C have the same instructions (worded differently) and the same questions, but the supplementary reasoning questions will help the child to understand and explain the differences between them.

The final activity is to number sort letters to make the postman's delivery job easier. You might say *If there was a letter for every flat in each multi-storey block how would the postman put them in order to deliver them?*
Block A – numbers 1–20 in sequence
Block B – 1, 3, 5, / 2, 4, 6 / 7, 9, 11 / 8, 10, 12 / 13, 15, 17 / 14, 16, 18 / 19, 21, 23 / 20, 22, 24
Block C – 1, 3, 5, 7 / 2, 4, 6, 8 / 9, 11, 13, 15 / 10, 12, 14, 16 / 17, 19, 21, 23 / 18, 20, 22, 24.
Ask the children: *What can you say about what is the same and what is different in Blocks B and C?*

DIFFERENTIATION
- Individuals or a small group may need to work on each block separately as one activity. The photocopiable sheet can be folded into three sections for this purpose.
- More confident children could use squared paper to investigate the question: *How many different ways could a block of 50 flats be arranged?*

NOW OR LATER
- The children could discuss tall buildings that they know, then find out how many floors each building has.
- Why do the children think flats are called flats?
- How many different kinds of home can the children name? (House, tower block, hostel, tenement and so on.)

Darts

RESOURCES AND CLASSROOM ORGANIZATION

Make one copy per child of photocopiable page 20, cut in half so that each dartboard can be used separately. You may need to write 'challenge' instructions on cards for groups of children (see below).

WHAT TO DO

Dartboard A. Say: *Write the number 20 in the bullseye* (indicate). *Now you have to fill in the other spaces. Each dartboard section must contain three numbers that add up to 20. You can't use the same number twice in one section.*

Dartboard B. Ask the children to count aloud in 10s to 100 and then write 100 in the bullseye. Now they have to fill in the other spaces with **multiples of 10** that add up to 100 in each section. Each section must have a different multiple.

For each activity, more detailed help may be offered. For example, you might suggest:

■ **Dartboard A**

Make all scores next to the Bullseye 10.

For the outer section, use the numbers 1–8.

■ **Dartboard B**

Make all the outer circle scores 10.

One section part must be 0 to make it work.

Conclude by setting the challenges for the children to work through underneath the dartboards. For Dartboard A, ask the children to record all of their 3-dart scores in the format: ... + ... + ... = 20. For Dartboard B, ask them to:

■ *Write down your highest 3-dart score outside the bullseye.*
■ *Write down your lowest 3-dart score outside the bullseye.*
■ *How many would you score with a 3-dart bullseye?*

Dartboards have double score sections; darts which land in them double the score. For dartboard A, ask the children to:

■ *Work out the double for the 10 score.*
■ *Work out the doubles for all the other sections except the bullseye.*
■ *Work out if there is a 3 dart doubles score larger than a 1 dart bullseye.*

For dartboard B, ask them to:

■ *Work out the doubles for sections 20, 30, 40, 50, 60, 70, 80, 90.*
■ *Work out double 0 (zero).*
■ *A 3 dart bullseye = 300. Find a 3 dart doubles score which is the same.*

These instructions can be written on card as a reminder if the children are working in groups.

DIFFERENTIATION

Some children may need to be supplied with all the three-number bonds of 20 (after working them out together) in order to complete Dartboard A. Other children may be able to use a higher target number (up to 50) for this dartboard. You can decide how much additional help to provide. Further discussion and support may also be necessary.

NOW OR LATER

Other activities using a dartboard format can be introduced, such as:

■ Explore the scoring sections on a real dartboard. Copy them onto a blank one.

■ Play darts where doubles and trebles are involved, using 3-dart scoring.

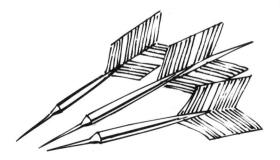

OBJECTIVES
To practise:
■ using number bonds to 20;
■ counting in 10s to 100.

CROSS-CURRICULAR
PSHE
Thinking skills.

GOING MENTAL? NO PROBLEM!

CLASSROOM ORGANIZATION
Make one copy per child of photocopiable page 21, perhaps enlarged to A3 size and cut into two sections.

WHAT TO DO
Before giving out the photocopiable sheet, review the terms **add, plus, take away, minus, subtract, makes** and **equals** with the class. Draw the mathematical sign for each of these on the board or flip chart (see Figure 9). You can choose whether to leave these as prompt cues or remove them before the children do the activity. The first two sections of the activity sheet both use these terms.

Distribute the activity sheet, indicate the first section and say: *Do these in your head without writing down the calculations. Just write your answers in the boxes.* Allow the children enough time to complete the section; then go through each problem, inviting the children to give their answers. Work through the second, more difficult section in the same way.

The third section challenges the children in a different way: the number problems are couched in word problems, which should be read aloud to the children one at a time. Each problem has two parts: deciding what calculation is needed and writing it in the space provided; then working out the answer and writing it in the appropriate box. Introduce this section by saying: *All of these problems can be solved using easy calculations. Your job is to work out what the easy calculation is and write it in here* (indicate the column). *Then you can work out the answer and write it in the box. I will read each problem to you, so that you can just think about the maths and not the reading.*

Afterwards, discuss each problem with the class. A good key question to ask is: *Will the answer be more or less than the biggest number in the problem?* This will help the children to see whether the calculation needed is addition or subtraction. You may decide to check the 'Write the calculation' column before the children work out the answers.

+	add
	plus
−	minus
	subtract
=	makes
	equals

Figure 9

DIFFERENTIATION
Help children to complete the number line and explain how they can use it to help them with the sums in each of the first two sections. Keep the prompt words visible for them to refer to. Allow sufficient time for slower children to do each part.

The children could work in pairs, setting each other challenges similar to those in each section of the photocopiable sheet.

NOW OR LATER
Play a team game where each child writes a mental word sum onto a piece of card with which to challenge another. Children from each team can choose who to ask or be assigned by the teacher. These cards could be shuffled and used randomly with the whole class to start a maths session.

100 SQUARE GAMEBOARDS

OBJECTIVES
To count to 100 forward and backwards:
- in odd numbers;
- in even numbers;
- in 10s.

CROSS-CURRICULAR
SCIENCE
Reasoning on patterns.

ENGLISH
Language development.

CLASSROOM ORGANIZATION
Make one copy per child of photocopiable page 22, and another (enlarged) copy of the gameboard. The children will need coloured pencils and will work in pairs.

WHAT TO DO
Give each child a copy of the photocopiable sheet and some coloured pencils. Introduce the gameboard idea by asking the children which board games they know or play at home. Answers may include draughts, chess, snakes and ladders and so on. Say: *Many board games have 100 squares that you move things around on to win. Look at your sheet. You have two gameboards with some instructions for playing. Let's read the instructions together.* Look at the gameboard and read instructions A and B, allocating one to each of the pairs of children. Draw attention to the different starting point for each one.

Tell the children that you will be asking them about the patterns when they have finished. Give them enough time to number and colour their gameboards and talk about the different number patterns. Conclude with a discussion, asking questions such as: *Can you describe the pattern your colours made? What was the same and what was different? Which game did this remind you of? Can you think of another game that would use this pattern?*

The children can use another copy of the gameboard (perhaps enlarged to A4 size) to design a game similar to snakes and ladders, then play it with a friend.

DIFFERENTIATION
The photocopiable sheet can be cut in half and the two gameboards used on different occasions. The instructions could be developed or modified, or the children could suggest other ways to find number patterns.

NOW OR LATER
- Look at a draughts or chess board. Ask the children to colour in the 100 square to make boards like this?
- They could find or create a picture to make into a 100-piece jigsaw. How will they do it?
- They could design a kitchen floor with 100 tiles.

Skittle scores

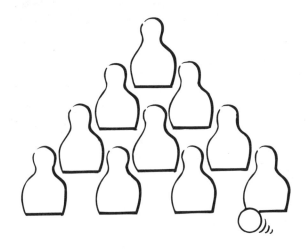

■ Number the skittles 1–10 in any order (randomly).
■ Now go bowling. Knock 2 skittles down to:

Score 6
Score 10

■ Draw skittles to:

Score 7	Score 12	Score 20

Investigation

Lowest score		Highest score

Lowest score		Highest score
Lowest score		Highest score

Pinball wizard

■ Write the numbers 1–9 in any order in the ◯.
Zig-zag through the middle: (+)/(−). Keep a
running score.

■ Put the numbers 10–90 in any order in the ◯.
Show which way to go.
Reach 100 to win.

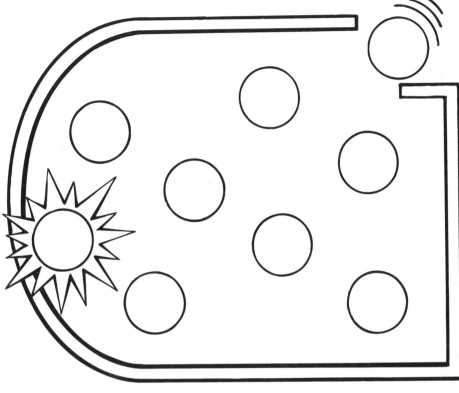

■ Work out
your running
score here:

Accumulated
score =

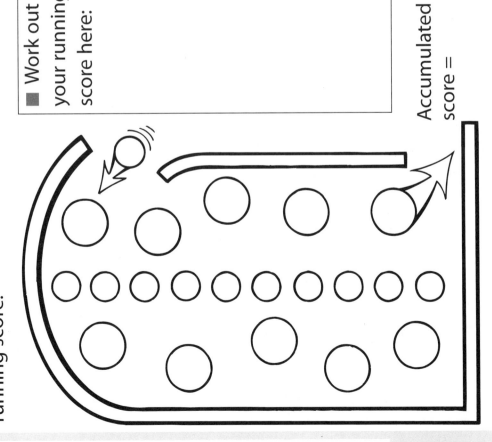

Caterpillar counting

Add 2

Add 3

Add 5

■ Put the number ◯ in the caterpillar's head. Count on.

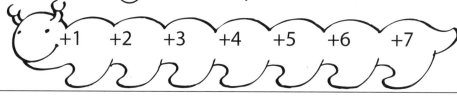

+1   +2   +3   +4   +5   +6   +7

Evens

+2   +4   +6   +8   +10   +12

Odds

+1   +3   +5   +7   +9   +11

+2   +1   +2   +1   +2   +1   +2   +1   +2

+3   +2   +1   +3   +2   +1   +3   +2   +1

■ What could you try in this caterpillar?

Ready to go! MATHS PUZZLES

Flats – an investigation

■ Follow the instructions.

Block A

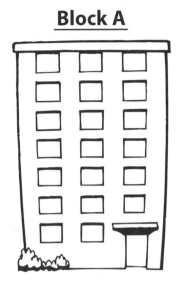

Block B

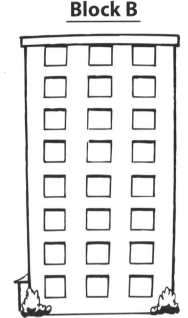

Block C

Number the flats in order from the bottom. Start at 1.

How many flats? ——
How many floors? ——
How many flights of stairs?   ——

Number the flats. Start at 1 at the bottom. Put odd numbers and even numbers on different floors.

How many flats? ___
How many floors? ___
How many flights of stairs?   ___

Number the flats. Start at 1. Put odd numbers on one floor, even numbers on the next floor.

How many flats? ___
How many floors? ___
How many flights of stairs?   ___

■ Help the postman sort out his letters. There is a letter for every flat. He needs to sort them like this:

Block A 1–20: in order.
Block B 1–24: 3 odd/3 even (1, 3, 5/2, 4, 6) and so on.
Block C 1–24: 4 odd/4 even (1, 3, 5, 7/2, 4, 6, 8) and so on.

■ Write **all** the flat numbers on small cards, mix them up in a postbag and then sort them for the postman.

Dartboards

Bullseye = 20. All sections add up to 20.

Bullseye = 100. All sections in 10s add up to the bullseye score.

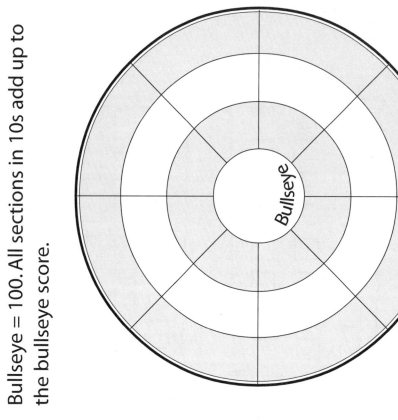

Bullseye

Bullseye

Challenge:

Challenge:

Going mental

Complete this number line first.

0 ⌐

    Add 3 to 4.   _____

    Take away 1 from 3.   _____

    Take away 3 from 7.   _____

    Five plus four.   _____

    8 minus 4.   _____

    10 minus 5.   _____

    ☐ + ☐ = 4

    ☐ + ☐ = 10

10 ⌐

    ☐ − 3 = 2

Complete this number line first.

10 ⌐

    Add 11 and 2.   _____

    Add 5 and 15.   _____

    Take away 2 from 12. _____

    Take away 1 from 20. _____

    Subtract 5 from 15.   _____

    ☐ + ☐ = 15

    16 − ☐ = 12

20 ⌐

    ☐ − 3 = 10

    ☐ − 0 = ☐

Read the problem:	Write the calculation:	Answer:
I have 6 marbles. I win 4 marbles. How many do I have now?		
I have 6 marbles. I lose 2. How many do I have now?		
My friend has 5 sweets. He gives me 1. How many are left?		
I buy a packet of 10 sweets. I eat 5 of them. How many are left?		
A football team has 11 players and 3 reserves. How many are in the team?		
There are eleven cricketers in a team. Six are out. How many are left in?		
Teacher gives us 20 spellings. I get 3 wrong. How many are right?		
I eat an apple every day for 2 weeks. How many apples is that?		
A dozen eggs is 12. How many is a half dozen?		
15 boys and 14 girls in a class. How many children altogether?		

100 square gameboards

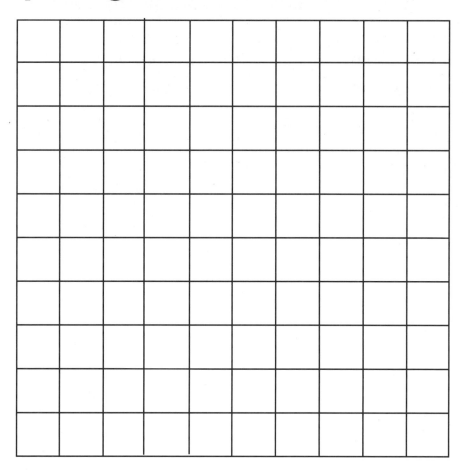

Instruction A

Number the squares 1–100. Start at the top.
Colour odd numbers in one colour. Colour even numbers in another colour.
Look at the pattern.
What games could you play?

Instruction B

Number the squares 1–100. Start at the bottom.
Colour all the 10s numbers in one colour. Colour all the 5s numbers in another colour. Look at the pattern.
What games could you play?

■ Use another gameboard to make a game that uses counters and dice. Write the instructions. Play it with a friend.

Pattern in number is a key skill area as it provides children with thinking strategies to produce visual formulas with which to approach many problem-solving activities. This section comprises 13 puzzle activities, 5 of which are accompanied by a photocopiable activity sheet for children to complete. All of the activities are focused on the Numeracy Strategy Framework's list of key objectives for shape and space in Years 1 and 2. These are as follows:

■ Explore pattern, shape and space.
■ Sort shapes and describe features.
■ Use one or more shapes to make a repeating pattern.
■ Make shapes, pictures, patterns.
■ Relate solid shapes to pictures.
■ Make models, fold for symmetry.
■ Recognize line symmetry.
■ Develop everyday language into maths language in connection with:
(i) 2D and 3D shapes (for instance cube, pyramid, hexagon)
(ii) position, direction and movement (for instance right/left turns or clockwise movements).

   The activities are not presented as a skill sequence and may be used in any way the teacher finds most useful to teach and consolidate the above skills.

SHAPES EVERYWHERE

RESOURCES AND CLASSROOM ORGANIZATION

Cut out four large shapes from sheets of sugar paper (see Figure 1). Each of these will be given to a group of children. Prepare a collection of real objects representing each of the shapes – for example, a shoe box containing a ball (circle/sphere), a cube and a pyramid shape. Print bold cards with the shape names **circle**, **square**, **rectangle**, **triangle**, **sphere**, **cube**, **box** and **pyramid**.

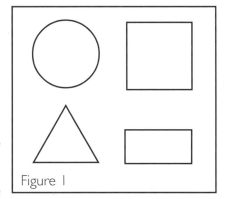

Figure 1

WHAT TO DO

Start the activity with a whole-class discussion and instruction. Hold up each large paper shape, asking the question: *Who knows this shape?* As each (2D) shape is identified, the appropriate name card should be selected and placed above each one on the board. Go on to discuss the first shape. You might say: *This is a circle. Many things are this shape. Look around – can you see any?* Draw two or three of the suggestions made by the children inside the large basic shape, leaving space for them to continue. Repeat this discussion for each shape.

   Divide the class into four groups and give each group one of the large shapes for them to add their own ideas. Encourage them to think beyond the classroom. After a short time, bring the class back together so that each group can show what objects they have drawn inside the shape. Display each shape as it is discussed.

   To conclude, produce the shoe box. Ask: *Which of the shapes is this most like?* Explain that the box is not a flat shape, but has height and depth. We call the flat shape **two-dimensional** (or **2D** for short) and the box shape **three-dimensional** (**3D**). Open the box and discuss the ball, cube and pyramid in the same way. Finally, use the name cards to label each 3D shape.

OBJECTIVES
■ To know the names of four basic 2D shapes and their 3D equivalents.
■ To relate these basic shapes to familiar objects.
■ To make sets based on shape criteria.

CROSS-CURRICULAR
DESIGN AND TECHNOLOGY
Observing artificial objects.

ENGLISH
Speaking and listening.

DIFFERENTIATION

■ During the session of group work, a fifth group might work with you (or another adult) in a more structured way to complete a shape (or more than one if time allows).
■ Groups could classify the objects further – for example, using categories such as Supermarket, Buildings, Vehicles and Toys. The children could record these sets using a large sheet of paper for each group. Supervise their work and help them to record their decisions.

NOW OR LATER

■ The children could make the 3D shapes in modelling clay.
■ They could use paper to construct a cube or pyramid, or use scissors to make snowflakes and doilies from folded paper circles.

SHAPE PICTURES

OBJECTIVES

■ To consolidate knowledge of basic 2D shapes.
■ To relate these shapes to 3D objects.

CROSS-CURRICULAR
SCIENCE
Representational diagrams.

ART
Shape pictures.

RESOURCES AND CLASSROOM ORGANIZATION

Each child will need a copy of photocopiable page 34, a card strip of the four shapes shown at the top of page 34, scissors, an envelope (to keep the card shapes in), some blank paper and a pencil.

WHAT TO DO

Distribute the card strips and show the children how to cut out each of the shapes (some children may require assistance). Ask them to practise drawing round each shape on a blank sheet of paper. You may remind them of the four 2D shape names by saying *Show me your triangle* and so on.

Now draw a few simple multi-shape diagrams, such as those in Figure 2. Encourage the children to look carefully at the shapes you have used to make these diagrams. Can they copy any of the pictures using their own shapes? Now ask them to try drawing around their own shapes to make other simple pictures of things.

Give out copies of photocopiable page 34. Ask the children to place their four shapes over the matching ones on the sheet. Draw their attention to the name beneath each shape. Now look together at the six boxes with named objects. Let the children work independently, using their shapes to make a picture in each of the boxes and then answering the 'How many?' questions at the bottom of the sheet. They can use each shape once, more than once or not at all in each picture.

Figure 2

DIFFERENTIATION

■ The four shapes may need to be supplied ready-cut to make sure that each has a neat edge for drawing around. Some extra practice may be needed for good pencil control.
■ Confident children could use blank paper to develop further representational ideas – for example, the Cat in the Hat, a cat on a mat or an ice-cream. They could work as a group to make a composite modern art picture, using all four shapes.

NOW OR LATER

■ The children could reduce pictures of real objects to their simplest shape forms.
■ They could design a 'Guess What?' game with simple shape pictures of objects.
■ They could use repeated shapes to make wallpaper patterns.

Picasso patterns

RESOURCES AND CLASSROOM ORGANIZATION

Prepare eight flashcards with the key vocabulary: **top, bottom, above, below, in front, behind, inside, outside**. Each child will need 10 small blank squares of paper and a pen or pencil.

WHAT TO DO

A sample 'picture' of cubist art might be used to begin discussions with the class. You could say *Look carefully at this interesting picture – it is mainly made up of shapes. Can you see them? Which ones can you see?* This will review the names of the four basic shapes: **circle, square, rectangle** and **triangle**. Introduce the positional vocabulary using your flashcards. Ask the children to listen carefully and draw exactly what you say. As an example, you might instruct the children to *Put a circle above a square*. Then ask them to check their response as you demonstrate it on the board, saying: *The square is below the circle.*

Continue with this whole-class instruction, increasing the difficulty of the task gradually while using all the key vocabulary opposites. Pay particular attention to the concept of 'in front and behind'. Use up to three shapes for each instruction. Your diagrams on the board will model the paired activity which follows.

Organize the children into pairs, and give each child 10 small blank squares of paper. A small screen (possibly a book) can be placed between each pair of children to increase the secrecy of the drawings and add to the fun. Each child should now draw a diagram with two or three shapes, as you have demonstrated. In turn, each child should then instruct his partner to draw the same picture – for example, by saying: *Draw a circle with a triangle on top of it.* Each instruction should use a word or phrase from one of the flashcards.

When the children have attempted to draw each other's pictures, the results should be passed over the screen and matched to the original drawings. The pairs should repeat the activity, alternating the drawing and instructing roles until all their 10 blank sheets are used up. The discussion between each pair will achieve valuable language learning. Listen in particular for the correct use of the flashcard vocabulary.

DIFFERENTIATION

■ You (or an assistant) may need to continue the initial instruction with a group, using only two of the shapes, before they are able to do the paired work with drawings.
■ Other children will be able to increase the number of instructions given in the paired work so that all four shapes are used in one drawing.

NOW OR LATER

■ Explore more positional opposites, such as **right and left**.
■ Look at the directions shown on maps, and discuss how compasses work. (See the activity 'Compass points' on page 28.)

OBJECTIVES
To use positional vocabulary.

CROSS-CURRICULAR LINKS

SCIENCE
Following precise instructions.

ENGLISH
Speaking and listening; comprehension.

ART
Shape pictures.

SHAPE CODES

RESOURCES AND CLASSROOM ORGANIZATION
Each child will need the envelope pack of four basic shapes from the activity 'Shape pictures' (page 24) and a copy of photocopiable page 35. The children could work in pairs, combining their sets of shapes.

WHAT TO DO
Make sure that each child (or pair) has an envelope with the four basic shapes: circle, square, rectangle and triangle. Ask the children to listen and arrange the shapes as you give them instructions.

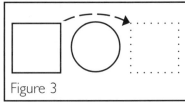

Figure 3

Start with an easy sequence. For example, say: *Take the square and put the circle next to it.* Demonstrate by drawing this on the board. *Now move the square to the other side of the circle. Let's draw it here...* (see Figure 3). Continue alternating the two moves until the pattern is evident. Ask a volunteer to continue the sequence on the board for a few more steps. Reinforce the idea by repeating the set of instructions. Let pairs of children try this out with one another for practice.

Give out copies of photocopiable page 35. Complete the first pattern box together by placing the shapes on top of the symbols, then physically moving each shape to its new position before drawing each shape to complete the pattern. Go on to discuss the rest of the sheet, one pattern box at a time, allowing time for the children to complete each one. Explain that shapes can be turned around in space, for example on their side or upside down (you could demonstrate). Two of the code patterns use this idea and children might want to use it when they draw their own code.

As a whole-class check, each pattern should be discussed and demonstrated from the children's own instructions.

DIFFERENTIATION
■ Some children may require supervision at all stages of this activity, and need more time and practice before they are able to complete the activity sheet. The sheet could be cut into single-pattern strips, and other patterns devised as appropriate. Repeat pattern work with beads, bricks or stickers will also support this activity.

NOW OR LATER
■ Test the children with patterns involving; longer repeat sequences, or use different symbols for the same sequences.
■ The children could find out about Morse code and how it works.

UNDER THE PYRAMIDS

RESOURCES AND CLASSROOM ORGANIZATION
Before you tell the story to the class, you will need to familiarize yourself with it and possibly elaborate on the outline given (see Figure 4) to plan your blackboard diagram. Each child will need a copy of photocopiable page 36.

WHAT TO DO
Tell this story to the class, building up a diagram on the board or flip chart as you go along:

An explorer went to Egypt. He saw the pyramids there, and asked a guide about them. The guide told him that some (but

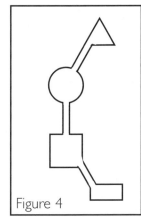

Figure 4

not all) of the pyramids had secret passages that went to the tombs of the ancient kings (Pharaohs). He decided to explore these secret passages. This is what he found. (Show how to build up the diagram here using Figure 4.) A secret passage went from a pyramid to a circular room. Around the walls of this room was a story, told in picture symbols (hieroglyphics), about the Pharaoh and how his tomb could be reached by going down the next secret passage. This passage went to a square room which was full of boxes and books: the Pharaoh's personal possessions. The last secret passage went from here to the tomb or burial room, where the Pharaoh's mummified body was placed. All of his wealth and treasures were in this oblong room.

Give out copies of photocopiable page 36 and read through the instructions. You may wish to refer to your diagram and do one of the tracking activities with the class. The children should realize that there are several possible routes, but that there can only be four 'secret passages' in all. The challenge of drawing the way out will show how well the children have understood the sequence of directions.

You could follow this by offering other maze picture stories, such as a cat chasing a mouse around the house to a hole; a mouse searching for cheese in various places.

DIFFERENTIATION
■ A group of children could complete the activity sheet together as you retell the story to them slowly.
■ You could adapt the story to give the 'secret passage' more (or fewer) stages.

NOW OR LATER
■ The children could draw a picture of each room under the pyramids.
■ They could tell the Pharaoh's story in words and pictures (hieroglyphics).
■ They could find out about pyramids and other buildings in ancient Egypt.

WALK THIS WAY

RESOURCES AND CLASSROOM ORGANIZATION
You will need to plot the children's suggestions on a large blank sheet of paper, a board or a flip chart. The children will need blank paper and pencils.

WHAT TO DO
Before starting, you may need to establish the directions **right** and **left** with the class.

Present the following problem for the whole class to consider: *A new child comes to our school and is put in our class. His Mum can only bring the child to the school gates. Once he is inside, he asks you which way to go. What will you say?*

As the children offer suggestions, a diagram can be built up. This will depend on the layout of your school. Figure 5 shows an example. When this is completed, ask different children to describe each change of direction using the terms 'right turn' and 'left turn'. They may plot each turn on your diagram as they do so.

Remove the diagram and ask the children to draw their own versions. Finally, ask them to describe the way from your classroom to the school office, library or hall, and to draw a similar plan showing this route.

OBJECTIVE
To plan a route using directional language.

CROSS-CURRICULAR
All subjects where following instructions is important (for example, science and PE).

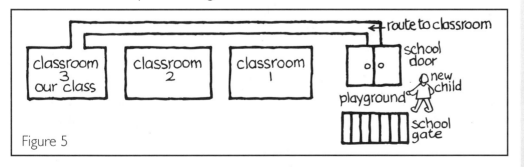

Figure 5

DIFFERENTIATION

■ Some children might need to be provided with a simple map of your school, so that they can mark the way to different suggested locations with coloured pencils.
■ More confident children could work in pairs, telling each other the way to school from home (using familiar landmarks). They could make simple route maps and explain them to the class.

NOW OR LATER

■ Explore further directional challenges, such as the way from home to a supermarket or to a friend's house.
■ Look at an atlas together, and talk about the directions of travel to other countries.
■ Find a map of your city centre with key places to visit, and ask the children to write directions for a tourist.

COMPASS POINTS

OBJECTIVE

To use the words North, South, East and West to describe position, direction and movement.

CROSS-CURRICULAR

GEOGRAPHY
Location and direction.

ENGLISH
Giving accurate instructions.

RESOURCES AND CLASSROOM ORGANIZATION

Each child will need a blank disk shape to draw around, a ruler and a pencil. Draw a large blank circle on the board or flip chart.

WHAT TO DO

Ask the children whether they know what you could use to help you if you were lost – say on a mountain, or on a ship at sea – so that you could work out which direction to go. They may suggest looking at the sun or the stars, or using a compass. Ask: *How could this help you?* Establish that the sun rises in the East and sinks in the West, that there is a North star, or that a compass will tell you which direction is North.

Discuss how a compass works. Explain, if necessary, that the needle in a compass always points to the North. Draw a vertical arrow in the circle to illustrate this; mark N for North at the tip. Ask the children what other directions they know besides North. Emphasize that opposite directions are often written in pairs: North and South, East and West. Draw and label the N to S line on the circle; then draw the E to W line and ask how it should be labelled (using the idea of the sun rising and sinking). The children should make observations about what you have done to the circle (halved and quartered it).

They can now prepare a blank compass by drawing round a disk. Say to them:
■ *The compass arrow always points North. Draw it and mark N clearly on your compass.*
■ *The opposite direction to North is South. Mark S where you think South is on your compass.*
■ *The sun rises in the East. Can you draw a sun in the right place and mark E on it?*
■ *The sun sets in the opposite direction, which is West. Where will you mark that?*

Now tell the children that a **line map** is a series of directions drawn as lines. Ask them to make a line map by following your directions with their index fingers on the table. For example, you might say *Go N, now go E, from here go S* or *Go W, now go S, from here go E, end up at the N.* The children could work in pairs to instruct each other in a similar way, drawing the line maps in pencil underneath their compass diagrams.

DIFFERENTIATION

Some children will find the four compass points enough to cope with; but others may be able to divide their compass into 8 parts, and use the points NE, NW, SE and SW to make their line maps more precise.

NOW OR LATER

■ The children could look at maps, find the N arrow and work out the other directions.
■ They could draw a Treasure Island map, with directions to find the treasure.
■ They could write about how a compass is useful.

PIE AND PIZZA

RESOURCES AND CLASSROOM ORGANIZATION

Each child will need a copy of photocopiable page 37, scissors and a pencil. You will need an apple and a knife for the initial demonstration. A circular pastry shape might be useful later. You may also wish to provide each child with an additional copy of the photocopiable page, so that cutting and writing are done on separate sheets.

WHAT TO DO

Introduce the activity by posing this problem to the children: *If you have only one apple and two children want to share it, how can this be done?* From the children's responses, you will reach a decision to cut the apple in half. Show them how to do this. Ask again: *Suppose there were four of you to share. How could you do that?* Demonstrate cutting the halves into quarters of the apple.

Now say that you are going to set the children another puzzle. Give each child a copy of the photocopiable sheet and a pair of scissors. Read out the first instruction on the sheet: *Dad makes an apple pie for 4 people. You are to make the pie lid.* Point first to the pie, then to the pie lid with the instruction 'cut out'. Explain that once the lid has been cut out, it should fit on top of the pie. Demonstrate how to cut out and fold the lid as you read out the 'Sharing the pie' instructions, and discuss how each part of sharing into halves and quarters should be done. Refer to how the apple was shared.

Read out the instruction for 'Sharing a pizza', which extends the same idea. Leave the children to work this out, using the same strategy and pie lid as before, but now sharing between 8 people.

DIFFERENTIATION

■ To achieve best results, some children may need assistance with accurate cutting and paper folding.
■ Other children could try cutting and folding other shapes (such as squares and hexagons) into fraction pieces.

NOW OR LATER

■ Sing the song 'Sing a Song of Sixpence' together. Draw the pie with 24 blackbirds coming out of it. Can the children say how many blackbirds might be in ½, ¼ or ⅛ of the pie?
■ The children can play a dice game in pairs, as follows. Cut the pie lid from the photocopiable sheet into eight pieces on the folds. Place it on the pie. Throw a dice and take off that number of pieces, until the last piece is gone.

OBJECTIVE
To understand fractions as parts of a shape.

CROSS-CURRICULAR
DESIGN AND TECHNOLOGY
Manipulation of scissors and paper shapes.

PSHE
Sharing.

THROUGH THE LOOKING GLASS

OBJECTIVE
To begin to understand lines of symmetry.

CROSS-CURRICULAR
ART
Spatial awareness in two dimensions.

PE
Spatial awareness in three dimensions.

RESOURCES AND CLASSROOM ORGANIZATION

You will need to prepare diagrams on the board or flip chart as shown in Figures 6 and 7. It will be helpful if the pie lid activity (see page 29) has already been done; otherwise, your explanation will need to be fuller. Each child will need blank paper, coloured pencils and a sheet of shapes as shown in Figure 8. Each pair of children will need a mirror and later an alphabet sheet of capital letters and numerals 0–9.

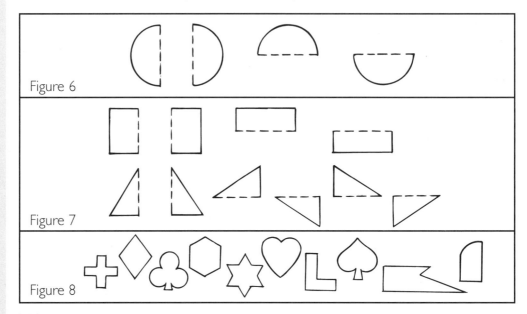

Figure 6

Figure 7

Figure 8

WHAT TO DO

Show the children your diagrams (see Figure 6). Explain that each shows a **line of symmetry** which divides the image into two halves which are identical (like in a mirror). Explain that part of each circle diagram is missing. Ask a child to complete each of your diagrams. The pie lid from the previous activity could be given to the child who volunteers to do the drawing, so that it can be referred to if necessary.

To develop the theme, draw diagrams of a part square and part triangle as shown in Figure 7 and ask the children to complete them, one at a time. As the diagrams are completed, use class discussion to emphasize the lines of symmetry (like the folds of the pie lid) and the idea that a shape is symmetrical when both halves are exactly the same. You can test this by introducing other shapes, asking *Which of these are symmetrical?* and suggesting that the children try to draw a line of symmetry.

Give each child a sheet of shapes, including non-symmetrical ones (see Figure 8). Ask them to use coloured pencils to shade in one side of each symmetrical shape.

DIFFERENTIATION

■ Children who find this activity difficult could be given a sheet of simple shapes (circle, square, rectangle, triangle, diamond and hexagon) to cut out and test for symmetry by folding down the middle.
■ More confident children could try to find a line of symmetry for familiar objects that they can draw, or for pictures. Let them test their lines with a mirror and draw conclusions.

NOW OR LATER

■ Try further investigations with pairs of children. Each pair will need a mirror and an alphabet sheet of capital letters. They should investigate which letters have a vertical and/or a horizontal line of symmetry. They should find that the letters A, H, M, O, T, U, V, W and Y have a vertical line of symmetry and the letters B, C, D, E, H, I, K, O and X have a horizontal line of symmetry. What do they discover about S and Z?
■ This investigation could be done with the numerals 0–9.

SQUARED PAPER SYMMETRY

RESOURCES AND CLASSROOM ORGANIZATION
Each child will need several sheets of 1cm squared paper, scissors and a coloured pencil.

WHAT TO DO
Show the children how to mark out a 6cm × 6cm square on squared paper and mark a line of symmetry across it, either horizontally or vertically. Ask them to make and cut out as many different squares like this as possible from one sheet. Now ask them to colour in one half of each square to show half of a simple shape. Demonstrate on the board or flip chart with one or two of the examples shown in Figure 9.

Let the children copy your example as their first try. They can work in pairs: each child prepares a half-pattern for his or her partner to complete. This can be repeated a number of times. Encourage the children to increase the complexity of their patterns (using more colours), to challenge their partner.

DIFFERENTIATION
■ Some children will need more practice in copying and marking prepared patterns before they design their own and try the pairs activity.
■ With other children, increase the complexity or the size of the pattern.

Figure 9

NOW OR LATER
■ Using the same pattern-building technique, the children could make a half-picture (for example, a houseboat star – see illustration) on squared paper for a partner to complete. The completed picture can then be folded along the line of symmetry, as in Figure 10.
■ They could try other papercraft folding and cutting activities to see what symmetry is produced.

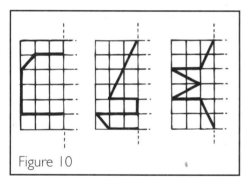

Figure 10

DISCOVERING TESSELLATING PATTERNS

RESOURCES AND CLASSROOM ORGANIZATION
Each child will need a supply of broad-lined writing paper (for drawing patterns) and several different-coloured pencils or crayons.

WHAT TO DO
Demonstrate to the children how to draw a simple repeat pattern sequence. A key instruction is to keep the pencil on the paper once the pattern has been started: this will help to maintain motor fluency and shape consistency. Once a line of the pattern is complete, turn the paper upside down and draw exactly the same pattern on the next line (it will be going the other way).

Give out broad-lined paper so that the children can copy what you have shown them, repeating it on a few lines until the

OBJECTIVE
To make simple repeating shape patterns that tessellate.

CROSS-CURRICULAR
ENGLISH
Handwriting and presentation.

ART
Border patterns.

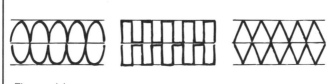

Figure 11

an overall pattern has become evident. Now discuss the way that the pattern produces spaces between shapes; these can then be coloured in to emphasize the pattern of main shapes and gap shapes. Try all the examples of repeating patterns shown in Figure 11.

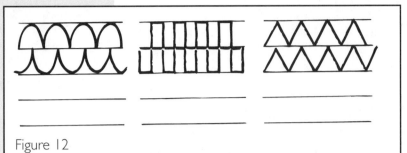

Figure 12

Another way of making a repeat pattern with shapes is to use a slight space shift between successive lines, as shown in Figure 12. The resulting pattern will be different. Encourage the children to try this.

Once the spaces produced by the varying patterns are coloured (using a 2 colour only choice) the tessellating effect will become evident and the children can be asked to describe the tessellating shapes and draw the conclusion that one side of each shape must form a side of the next shape if it is to tessellate.

DIFFERENTIATION

■ The size of the paper, pencils or crayons and guiding lines or squares will require careful consideration for children with poor motor control. A guiding adult hand may be needed to ensure success.

■ Other geometric shapes (such as hexagons) could be introduced, and a patchwork quilt pattern of **tessellating** shapes (where one side of each shape forms a side of the next shape) could be produced.

NOW OR LATER

■ The children could explore patterns in joined-up handwriting, using different repeated sequences of letters such as (m n u h) (v w x z) (o c e s) or (b d p q). They could use colours to show the different repeating shapes.

■ They could produce tessellating pattern designs for fabric, wallpaper, floor coverings or knitted sweaters.

SQUARING THE SQUARE

OBJECTIVES
■ To extend visual reasoning.
■ To develop problem-solving strategies.

CROSS-CURRICULAR
SCIENCE
Reasoning skills.

RESOURCES AND CLASSROOM ORGANIZATION

This game can be demonstrated on the floor and then played on tables. All the sticks used need to be the same length: rulers for the floor game or drinking straws for the table games. Each child will also need a dotted sheet (see Figure 14) to take home.

WHAT TO DO

This puzzle game is a variation on the well-known pencil and paper game of 'Boxes'. Demonstrate it to the class by playing against three volunteers. Each of you will need a pile of sticks, all of the same length (rulers will do). You could mark out a square

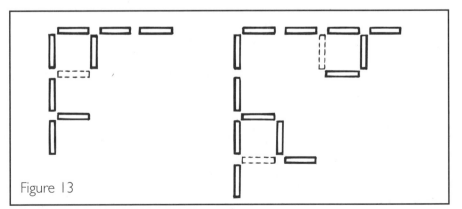

Figure 13

with chalk on the floor as an outline the size of 3 × 3 sticks. This is the gameboard.

Start by putting down one stick (vertically or horizontally, not diagonally) to make the edge of the square. Each child must follow your example. The rule is that every placed stick must touch another at one corner. With a 3 × 3 square, there can only be 3 sticks down and 3 across before you start 'squaring the square' – that is, filling in the small central square section. The aim for each player is to complete a 'box' or small square and score a point, while also trying to prevent others from doing the same. The difficulty increases as you progress through the game (as Figure 13 shows).

Repeat the demonstration with new players; then repeat with a 4 × 4 square size. The children can now work in pairs, using the drinking straws or their tables. This will increase their concentration and strategic skills as they pit their wits against each other.

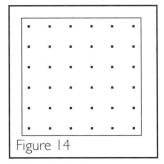

Figure 14

DIFFERENTIATION

■ Adult supervision and participation in the game, with discussion on strategy, may be needed for each new square size that is tried.

■ Confident children could try playing a similar game with another shape (for example, a triangle or a hexagon). Does the game still work?

NOW OR LATER

Give each child a dotted sheet as shown in Figure 14. They can use this to play the game at home, or on a long journey!

AN EASTER EGG TANGRAM

OBJECTIVE
To be aware of possible shapes within shapes.

CROSS-CURRICULAR
DESIGN AND TECHNOLOGY
Model making.

RESOURCES AND CLASSROOM ORGANIZATION

Each child will need a copy (on card) of photocopiable page 38, a piece of card to support the base of the egg, colouring materials, scissors and paste.

WHAT TO DO

This activity can be introduced to the class at the appropriate time through a general discussion about Easter eggs. Give out copies of the photocopiable sheet. Explain that the blank egg should be ignored at first, but the marked egg is a puzzle which needs to be coloured in a special way. Say: *Each black line marks the edge of a colouring space, so your colour or pattern must not go over it into the next space. Every space must have a different colour or pattern.*

Give the children plenty of time to complete the colouring before going on to the next step: cutting around the outline of the egg before cutting across each of the black lines, so that a nine-piece tangram puzzle is produced. Each child should mix up the pieces and then try to fit them back together inside the blank egg. The colours and patterns may help to jog the child's memory! They can then try each other's tangrams.

DIFFERENTIATION

■ Adult help and supervision at every stage of this activity will ensure successful completion and understanding of the puzzle concept.

■ Some children could rearrange the tangram pieces to make new shapes, such as imaginary creatures that have hatched from the egg.

NOW OR LATER

The children can use make a puzzle greeting card from their sheet. They should make the tangram as before, but place the nine puzzle pieces in a small pocket stapled to the back of the blank egg. The card can be supported by a cross-piece.

Shape pictures

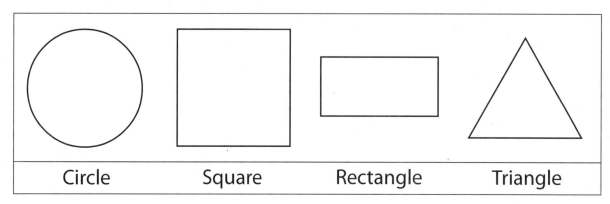

| Circle | Square | Rectangle | Triangle |

Xmas tree	Candle	Firework
Flower in pot	Witch's hat	Jack-in-the-box

■ Look at your pictures:

How many circles have you drawn? _____

How many squares have you drawn? _____

How many rectangles have you drawn? _____

How many triangles have you drawn? _____

Shape codes

■ Continue the pattern to the end of each box.

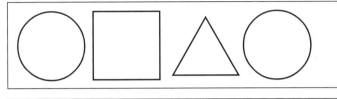

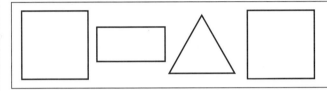

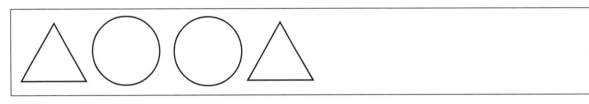

■ Now look carefully at these. Some shapes have turned around.

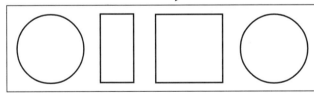

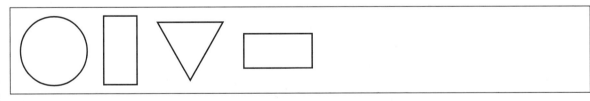

■ Make a pattern for your partner to continue.

Under the pyramids

■ Explore the pyramid and draw the secret passages to the tombs.

This is the way to go: △ ➡ ◯ ➡ □ ➡ ▭

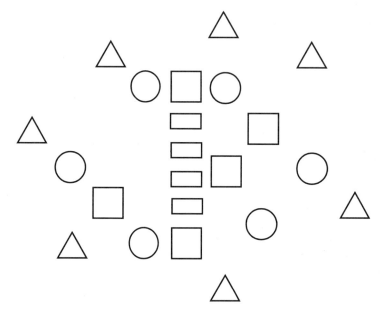

Hint: not all the pyramids have secret passages.

You can use each shape only once in each passage.

■ Start at the tomb and draw which way you need to go to get back to the outside.

■ Draw your own maze here, showing where to go in.

Ready to go! MATHS PUZZLES

Name   Date

Pie and pizza

Dad makes an apple pie for four people.
You are going to make the pie lid.

Cut out

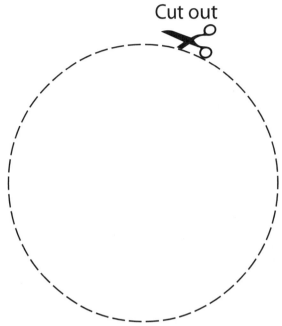

Sharing the pie

Fold the lid to help you.
Cut the pie in half – draw
the knife cut.
Cut the pie equally the
other way.

■ Draw one cut-out
piece here:

Sharing a pizza

Send out for a pizza.
Share it between 8 people.
How will you cut it?

An Easter egg tangram

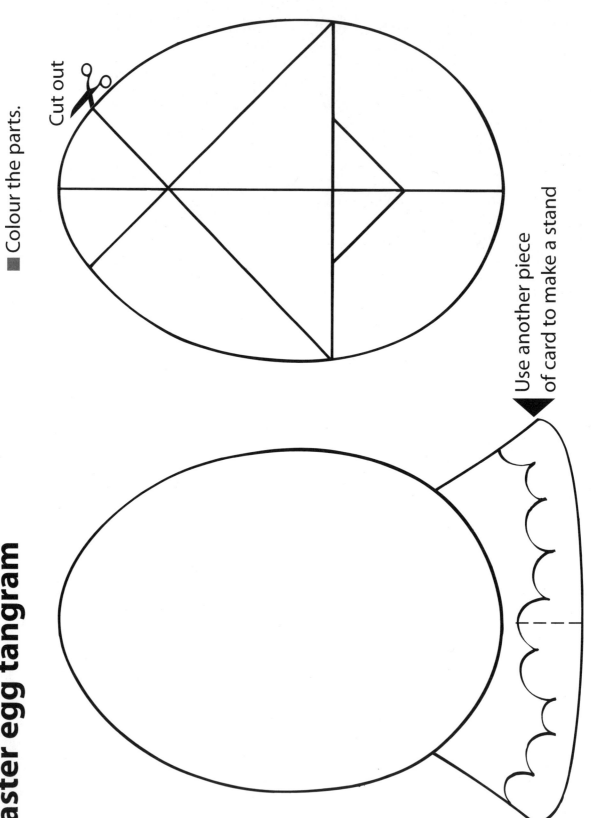

Name

Date

■ Colour the parts.

Cut out

Use another piece
of card to make a stand

APPROACH TO MEASURES

This section comprises 10 puzzle activities, 5 of which are accompanied by a photocopiable activity sheet for the children to complete. Most of the activities involve discussion between the teacher and the class, or between children in groups and pairs, so that the children can easily assimilate the language of standard metric units for the appropriate task. Their familiarity with this language is checked by the final activity, 'Mental measure' (page 47). All of the activities are focused on the Numeracy Strategy Framework's key objectives for measuring in Reception, Year 1 and Year 2. These are as follows:
- Comparing and ordering everyday measures.
- Suggesting suitable standard or uniform non-standard units and measuring equipment to estimate, then measure length, mass or capacity.
- Understanding and using the vocabulary of standard measure (for example metre, gram, litre).
- Using a ruler to draw and measure lines to nearest cm.
- Reading other scale measures to nearest label division.
- Time relationships: days, weeks, months, years, seconds, minutes, hours (analogue and digital) $\frac{1}{2}$ and $\frac{1}{4}$ hours.
  A mental maths check has been provided to review the vocabulary and skills.

PORTABLE MEASURES

RESOURCES AND CLASSROOM ORGANIZATION

You will need to provide string or wool, scissors, Sellotape and a tape-measure or ruler for each pair of children, and a copy of photocopiable page 48 for each child.

WHAT TO DO

Organize the children into pairs. Give each child a photocopiable sheet. Show the children the materials you are giving them to complete these measuring tasks.

Choose one pair of children to demonstrate the tasks. Ask them to show you how they would use the string to measure each other: from elbow to wrist; foot (**not** shoe) length; and around the fist. As each measure is made (with your assistance), and any necessary adjustments are agreed on and made, the string can be cut to the measured length. Both children can do this, giving you two lengths for each of the tasks. Hold up each pair of lengths and let the other children comment on the difference between them.

The children will now be ready to carry out these measuring tasks. Tell them to compare each other's lengths as they make them, before they follow the activity sheet's instruction to fix each piece of string to their own sheet after cutting along the scissor line and compare these lengths. The final question *What do you see?* provides a discussion point when the task is complete.

The bottom part of the photocopiable sheet repeats the measuring activity with longer lengths: from head to toe; from the middle left fingertip to the middle right fingertip when the arms are stretched; from the nose to the middle right fingertip when the arms are stretched; and from the thumbtip to the little fingertip when the fingers are spread. The children will need to work in pairs to make accurate measurements. Once the informal comparisons have been made as before, a tape-measure or ruler can be used to convert to standard units. Ask the children:
- *Are any of the lengths the same? If so, which ones?*
- *How might this be useful for us?*
- *What do the numbers on the tape-measure mean?*
You may further the discussion with this information: *In the past, many units were based*

OBJECTIVES
- To use informal measures to compare body sizes.
- To begin to formalize the measuring of length using a tape measure, ruler and height chart.

CROSS-CURRICULAR
PSHE
Awareness of self and others.

SCIENCE
Structure of the human body.

HISTORY
Measures used in the past.

on the measurements of parts of the body. They were not accurate because people varied in size, and standard units were introduced to help trade and to prevent cheating. Standard length metal bars are set into a wall on one side of Trafalgar Square, London. A **fathom** *was based on the span of a man's outstretched arms. A* **mile** *was based on 1000 paces made by a Roman soldier. These old units have now been replaced, for most purposes, by metric measurements.*

DIFFERENTIATION
■ Some children will need adult assistance in these practical tasks to improve their discussion and learning.
■ Other children could find out the measures used by tailors and dressmakers, exploring these in practical situations.

NOW OR LATER
■ The children could research the history of measures of length and distance, relating what they discover to their experience. For example, can they suggest a practical basis for such measures as the span, cubit, foot and yard?

JUST MY SIZE!

OBJECTIVE
To make size comparisons and use comparative vocabulary.

CROSS-CURRICULAR
PSHE
Self-awareness.

SCIENCE
The human body.

ENGLISH
Speaking and listening.

RESOURCES AND CLASSROOM ORGANIZATION
The children will need sheets of stiff A3 paper, pencils and scissors. They should work in table groups.

WHAT TO DO
Give each child a sheet of stiff A3 paper. Ask the children to fold the sheet in half. Demonstrate drawing round your hand on the board or flip chart, and write your name inside the drawing. Explain to the children that they are going to do the same thing on one half of their sheet and then draw round their foot on the other half. They should then use the scissors to cut out each drawing carefully.

The children at each table can now compare their hand and foot sizes. Assist the discussion by writing comparative vocabulary on the board or flip chart: *big, bigger, biggest; large, larger, largest; small, smaller, smallest.* Ask questions such as: *On your table, who has the biggest/smallest hand? Can you find someone in the class with a bigger/ smaller one? Can you place all the hand drawings on the table in a line, from the smallest to the largest?*

Let the children from each table line up in order of height to see whether this matches the hand and foot order. Collect up all the cut-outs to make comparisons across the whole class. They could be used to make a large chart, with the vocabulary *Small, Medium, Large* used for the hand shapes and actual shoe sizes (supplied by the children) for the foot shapes. This visual data can be discussed by the children.

Children could use a height chart to measure taller and shorter children, and compare the height differences with those between the same children's hand and foot sizes (from the charts), then draw conclusions.

DIFFERENTIATION

■ Some children may require adult assistance with the practical tasks of drawing and cutting.

NOW OR LATER

■ The children could draw round both of their hands to make a pair of paper gloves.
■ They could use the foot outline to draw a pair of socks, then cut these out and compare each other's sock sizes.
■ Make a chart of the height of all the children in the class.

CLASSROOM MEASURE

RESOURCES AND CLASSROOM ORGANIZATION

You will need to make a list of the classroom furniture and write each type of item (*big table, small table, bookcase* and so on) on an A5 card, then put the cards in a box or bag. Make a large diagram showing a bird's-eye view of the classroom. Each group of children will need a ball of string, scissors and a packet of drinking straws.

WHAT TO DO

Tell the children that you are looking for ways to change the classroom space. Ask: *How do you think this can be done?* Elicit the response that the best way would be to move the furniture around. Ask them to help you plan how this might be done. Divide the children into table groups and give them the task of measuring certain items of furniture with the equipment you will provide.

One child from each group can take a card from the box or bag; this will tell them which item to measure. All the groups should begin their task at the same time. Note any group having difficulty, or any group discussing a strategy before they begin (refer to this in the class discussion later on). The children should record their investigation briefly on the card (there may be more cards than groups). Some groups will be able to measure more than one item.

When all the collected information is fed back, write it on the classroom plan. Now return to the initial challenge of rearranging the furniture: ask the children to make suggestions. Using the data, discuss the feasibility of each suggestion and the effects it would have in practice. Finally, thank the children for their hard work and ask them to record their ideas on drawing paper, as you can't remember them all! This may lead to a real classroom rearrangement!

DIFFERENTIATION

■ Children working in mixed-ability groups will be supported by their peers. A support assistant may also be needed to supervise and suggest ways of working.
■ More confident children could measure the classroom perimeter (using the same units of reference), and use this to map the classroom with the furniture marked out to scale on blank or squared paper.

NOW OR LATER

■ The children could replan their own bedrooms, drawing 'before' and 'after' diagrams.
■ They could design a garden, incorporating features such as a lawn, pond, rockery, vegetable plot and barbeque space.
■ They could design a playground, keeping safety in mind.

OBJECTIVES

■ To use informal units of length measurement.
■ To begin to understand the concepts of area and perimeter from a real-life investigation.

CROSS-CURRICULAR PSHE

Safety issues, co-operation.

DESIGN AND TECHNOLOGY

Arranging furniture.

BREAKFAST CEREALS

RESOURCES AND CLASSROOM ORGANIZATION

Some time before you intend to explore this theme, ask the children to provide empty breakfast cereal boxes (which may be used later for design and technology work). When you have collected boxes for a variety of different cereals, try this activity. Provide a large sealed bag of sugar or salt.

WHAT TO DO

In this activity, children will investigate the size of packaging in a variety of food products and draw conclusions. Introduce the theme by asking the children to name their favourite cereal. You could make a list and use tally marks to show how popular each cereal is.

Show the collection of boxes to the children, and ask one child to come and read the number on the spine or top of a box. Explain that this number is usually followed by **g**, and that it tells you how much cereal there is in the box: the **g** stands for **grams**. Place all the boxes with the same **g** number next to each other and compare their sizes. These will probably vary, so ask: *If we choose the biggest box of these, will we get the most cereal? ...Why not? What can you tell me about the packaging? Why would you need a bigger packet for a small amount?*

If possible, show the children a large sealed bag of sugar or salt. Let them feel its weight and look at the weight figure. How does this packet compare with the cereal boxes? Encourage the children to make observations about packet size and weight, such as: 'The packet size doesn't tell you how much is inside, it's the **g** number that tells you.'

Now ask the children to **estimate** how many cereal boxes would have the same weight as the sugar or salt. Sugar comes in 1kg packs and salt can be 2kg so there could be a calculation from grams to kilograms. Draw the sugar or salt and the equivalent weight of boxed cereal on a shelf, and talk about the amount of cupboard space each takes up. Ask: *What is your conclusion?* The children should find that size of packaging and mass in products varies – bigger does not necessarily mean more.

DIFFERENTIATION

Ask the children to make lists of the weights of supermarket products at home. Explain the term **net weight**. Compare the weights of similar products from different supermarket chains. Ask them to: *Consider why many products have a net weight of 586g.*

NOW OR LATER

■ The children could imagine filling a cupboard with their favourite provisions, list these and think about weights and prices.
■ They could design a box for a new breakfast cereal.

TEA AND BISCUITS

OBJECTIVE
To explore capacity and mass in a real-life context.

CROSS-CURRICULAR
PSHE
Cooking and hospitality.

ENGLISH
Drama and discussion.

RESOURCES AND CLASSROOM ORGANIZATION

Prepare a small table for a pretend tea party with a tablecloth, a teapot, four plastic cups or beakers, two paper plates and some real biscuits (one for each child). Keep a jug of cold water nearby. Prepare two biscuit recipe cards as shown in Figure 1, and bring in a biscuit cutter.

WHAT TO DO

Explain to the children that you are having four people to tea and you need their help. Ask: *How will I know how much water I need to fill the teapot?* Encourage them to try out any suitable suggestions, such as:
- filling the teapot (to a marked level) and seeing how many cups you can fill from it;
- pouring four full cups into the teapot.

Ask the children to explain what conclusion they have reached. Extend the problem by saying that you are inviting eight people to your tea party. *How many teapots will I need? How many for 16 people? How many for 32 people?* Take this as an approximate value of the class size, and make a diagram to show how you reached the number of teapots needed for a class tea party.

At a party, there is usually food. Introduce the next part of the activity: *Now let's talk about the biscuits for the tea party. Here are the recipes I would use to make them.* Display the two recipe cards as shown in Figure 1. Say to the children that each recipe tells you how much of each ingredient to mix together to make biscuits. Tell them that you will use the same biscuit cutter for both recipes (show them the cutter).

Ask: *Which recipe will give me more biscuits? How do you know? What other ingredients could we add to make the biscuits tastier?* Children may suggest jam, chocolate chips, ginger, cream and so on. Ask them to choose one of the recipes, copy it out and add a new ingredient, then draw a biscuit for a recipe book. Conclude by giving out the biscuits you have provided.

DIFFERENTIATION

A support assistant may need to help less confident children complete the biscuit task and discuss the outcomes further.

NOW OR LATER

- The children could role-play a series of tea parties, with a different number of guests each time.
- Read the account of the Mad Hatter's tea party in *Alice in Wonderland* together. Dramatize it and act it out.

Biscuit X
200g flour
75g butter
75g sugar
A pinch of salt
3–4 tablespoons water

Biscuit Y
200g flour
100g butter
150g sugar
A pinch of salt
1 large egg

A biscuit recipe
Mix the _____ and _____
Add the _____ and _____
Use _____ to make the mixture soft.
Add (any extra ingredient).
Roll out and cut shape with cutter.
Place on baking tray. Bake in oven.

Figure 1

CHANGE MACHINES

OBJECTIVES
■ To recognize coins of different values.
■ To exchange some coins for a coin of an equivalent total value.

CROSS-CURRICULAR
ART
Rubbings.

PSHE
Using money.

RESOURCES AND CLASSROOM ORGANIZATION

Provide a collection of plastic money in a variety of coin denominations. Each child will need a copy of photocopiable page 49, blank paper and a pencil.

WHAT TO DO

Give each pair of children some plastic money. Tell them that you are going to ask them to use the small value coins. Ask: *Which coin has the smallest value?* (1p). *Is this the smallest in size? ...Which one is smaller?* Pick up this coin (5p).

Let each pair work together: one child holds up a 5p coin while the other chooses coins that he or she thinks have the same total value. They should then compare what they are holding and see whether they agree or disagree that the exchange is correct. They should repeat this using different combinations, such as 2p + 2p + 1p and 1p + 1p + 1p + 1p + 1p.

Give each child a piece of paper and demonstrate the coin rubbing process. Ask the children to 'rub' the different coin combinations for 5p that they have discovered. Ask: *Which side of a coin shows its value?* Suggest that this is the best surface to 'rub'. This provides practice for the activity which follows. Give each child a copy of the photocopiable sheet, and introduce the activity by saying: *These machines give change from big-value coins. Place the right coin at the top of the machine and 'rub' it. Now you have to decide what small change you want and 'rub' those coins in the box underneath. You can try two different ways of getting change for 10p and 20p. Notice that the 20p and 50p machines do not give 1p or 2p coins.*

DIFFERENTIATION

■ To build children's confidence, pairs could repeat the initial activity before they work individually on the 'change machines'. The photocopiable sheet could be attempted in parts, and cut for this purpose.
■ More copies of the photocopiable sheet could be provided to let children cover all the change possibilities. They could also investigate £1 and £2 coin machines, trying to find all the possible variations (without 1p, 2p or 5p coins).

NOW OR LATER

■ The children could role-play a bus journey, with the driver or conductor giving tickets and change for journeys.
■ Look at some foreign coins. Discuss what they are worth in sterling.
■ The children could design a £5 coin.
■ They could try other rubbings such as embossed wallpaper medals or badges.

JELLY BEAN MIXTURE

OBJECTIVE
■ To use vocabulary related to mass.
■ To solve a simple word problem.

CROSS-CURRICULAR

SCIENCE
Classifying data.

DESIGN AND TECHNOLOGY
Relating colour and flavour.

RESOURCES AND CLASSROOM ORGANIZATION

Each child will need a copy of photocopiable page 50 and five coloured crayons (red, blue, yellow, green and purple).

WHAT TO DO

Give out the photocopiable sheet and explain the task: *This jar of jelly beans has equal amounts of five different flavours (and colours): red cherry, blueberry, banana yellow, green apple and purple grape. Each jelly bean weighs 1g. There is a 100g mixed bag, and it needs to be split up into five separate flavour bags all weighing the same. Can you do it? Write the flavour on each new pack.*

The children should draw 20 beans in each of the five empty bags, and colour each set of beans differently. They can tahen label each 20g. In the concluding discussion children should also explain the methods they used to sort out colours and flavours.

DIFFERENTIATION
More confident children could divide up a larger amount of jelly beans (250g) into the same five flavours; or sort the contents of five single-flavour 100g bags into five mixed-flavour 100g bags.

NOW OR LATER
■ The children could think of more sweet flavours and give them appropriate colours.
■ They could collect sweet packets for a 'Tuck shop' game, listing the prices.
■ They could advertise a new sweet product to appeal to children everywhere.

TIMESPAN

RESOURCES AND CLASSROOM ORGANIZATION
Each child will need a copy of photocopiable page 51 and some coloured pencils or crayons. Provide a list of the months of the year.

WHAT TO DO
Start with a general discussion that gets the children thinking about how long periods of time are. Ask questions such as: How old are you? How long is a year? When is it Christmas? What do we do in the summer? How long does it take for flowers to grow in the spring? What does 'a long time' mean? Suggest the idea of breaking down a long time into shorter periods of time. Draw a pictorial time sequence on the board or flip chart to show how this can be done (Figure 3 shows suitable examples).

Give out copies of the photocopiable sheet. Explain that the five babies shown at the top of the sheet were all born in the year 2000. To list them in birthday order, the children need to know the sequence of months in the year. Talk them through the questions which follow, helping any child who cannot see how to work out the answers. Finally, discuss the characteristics of the four seasons (weather, plant growth, clothing) before the children draw pictures on the 'season plate'. Ask them to write which months they think cover each season of the year.

DIFFERENTIATION
Some children may need help ordering the months of the year using the list. They may do this by ordering the birthday months of a small group. Other children may work out the numbers of days in each month from a calendar and the numbers of days in one year.

NOW OR LATER
■ The children could make a picture calendar to mark special occasions in the year.
■ They could try to work out how many months they have been alive.

OBJECTIVES
■ To know the months and seasons of the year.
■ To know how time is measured in days, months and years.

CROSS-CURRICULAR
SCIENCE
Animal and plant growth.

GEOGRAPHY
Weather.

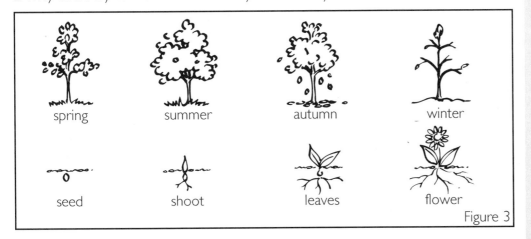
Figure 3

HOW LONG DOES IT TAKE?

OBJECTIVE
To be able to read the time on both analog and digital clocks.

CROSS-CURRICULAR
SCIENCE
Patterns of human daily life.

PSHE
Personal differences.

RESOURCES AND CLASSROOM ORGANIZATION
Once the key times of day have been agreed on, you will need to duplicate a diary sheet with blank clocks and digital boxes for the children to take home.

WHAT TO DO
Ask the children: *What happens in your day? Let's say it's a school day and start right at the beginning.* Record their responses in a list. Then work with the children to edit the list down to about seven or eight 'key times', such as: Get up, Have breakfast, Come to school, Go home, Have tea, Watch TV and Go to bed. You might repeat the process for a weekend day.

Use this discussion to form the basis of the time diary that you want the children to collect individually as homework. For each key time, there should be analog and digital spaces (as shown in Figure 4).

Allow the children ample (but not too much) time to complete their time diary at home. Set a time for its return. When the diaries are returned, discuss (as a class) how the individual records vary. Suitable questions to raise at this time include: *How long does it take you from getting up to having breakfast? How long are you at school? How long do you watch TV for before going to bed? How long do you think you are asleep for?*

Encourage the children to work out the time between each of their personal recordings and the next, and to compare these times with other children on their table. The first afternoon recording will help them to understand and compare the 12-hour and 24-hour clocks. The activity will show them how the day is divided between activities such as sleeping, playing, working and coming to school. If both schoolday and weekend time diaries are made, each child can make a personal comparison of the different days.

Get up.

Have breakfast.

Come to school.

Figure 4

DIFFERENTIATION
Encourage the children to involve parents or older siblings in their recording homework. Some children may wish to record more times than the basic items agreed upon, making their personal diaries more detailed.

NOW OR LATER
■ The children could make a personal diary of 'favourite activities' and work out how long they usually last.
■ Can they work out how long they spend asleep in a week?
■ They could choose different (imaginary or real) people and write 'A Day in the Life of...' diary entries.

MENTAL MEASURE

RESOURCES AND CLASSROOM ORGANIZATION

Make one copy of photocopiable page 52 (perhaps enlarged to A3 size) for each child. Decide how many sections you want to cover at a time, and cut the sheet accordingly. You will need to prepare a large prompt sheet for Section A with the vocabulary **m = metre, cm = centimetre, g = gram, kg = kilogram** and **l = litre**. Work on Section C needs to be prompted with the words **more, less** and **same**.

WHAT TO DO

To start the initial discussion, show the children your prepared prompt sheet. Ask them to read the words you are showing them. Tell them that they will need these words to complete the puzzles you will give them. Distribute copies of the photocopiable sheet (or just part A), and read through the ten puzzles. Now tell the children: *Pick up your pencils and start.* Leave the prompt sheet visible for them to copy from if they need to. Allow sufficient time for this part to be completed before checking the answers with the whole class. Children may come and indicate the correct answer on your prompt sheet as you do this.

Section B presents calculation problems which use different units to familiarize the children with addition and subtraction in measure. This part can be completed following a brief review of the vocabulary and abbreviations which appear in each problem; read through the 10 questions before the children begin.

Section C is aimed at finding out if children understand and can compare different measurements by making a decision about whether one is more or less or the same as the other, then solving some simple word problems.

SUPPORT AND EXTENSION

The photocopiable sheet can be presented in three parts. An adult assistant could cover each problem individually in order to review and rework the skills needed to complete it.

NOW OR LATER

■ Put the children into 'measure groups' to explore the theme creatively. They could draw pictures, extend their vocabulary, make comparisons, present a talk and so on.
■ Make a simple board game with measure puzzles on several squares, and play it with a group of children.
■ Prepare a set of puzzle and answer cards. Use them to play 'Snap', matching puzzles with answers.

OBJECTIVE
To review the vocabulary and basic units of measure.

CROSS-CURRICULAR

ENGLISH
Vocabulary extension and spelling.

SCIENCE
Understanding different kinds of measure: length, mass and capacity.

Portable measures

■ Use string to measure:

elbow to wrist	foot (not shoe)	around fist

✂ -

■ Fix one end of the string to the • mark on the picture. Let it hang.
■ Compare the lengths. What do you see?

■ Use string to measure:
1. Head to toe.
2. Right to left hand (arms stretched).
■ Compare the lengths.
Use a tape-measure to check.
■ Now measure:
1. Nose to middle finger. _____
2. A handspan. _____

WORDS YOU NEED
long
longer
shorter
same
centimetre (cm)

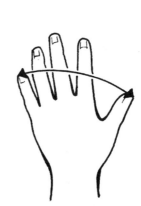

Change machines

You put a large coin in the top of the machine to get change.

■ Rub the coins you might get from each machine.

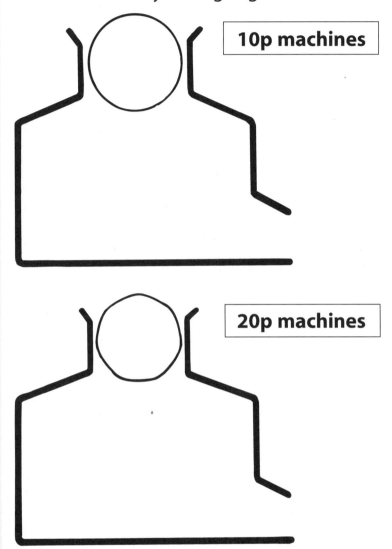

10p machines

20p machines

Note: No 1p or 2p coins in these machines.

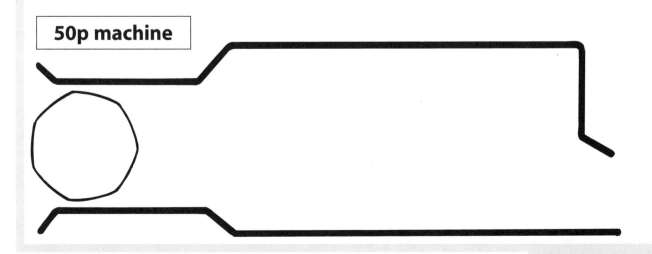

50p machine

Name

Date

Jellybean sort

The jar in the middle contains 100 mixed beans, weighing 100g.

■ Sort the flavours into separate bags, with the same number of beans in each bag.

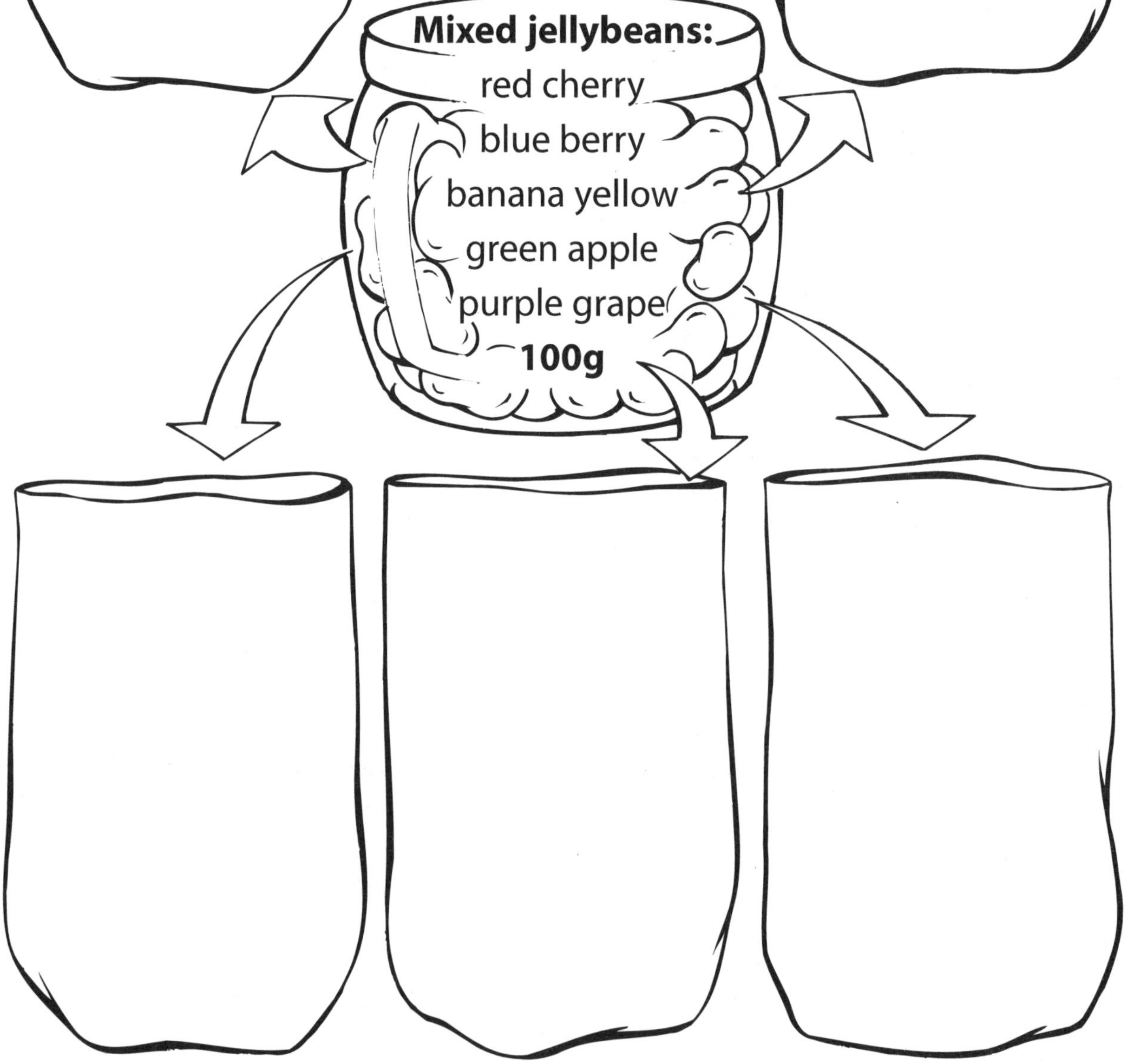

Mixed jellybeans:
red cherry
blue berry
banana yellow
green apple
purple grape
100g

■ How many jellybeans are there in each bag? _____

Timespan

Here are five Millennium babies.

■ List them in birthday order:

1_____   2_____   3_____

4_____   5_____

■ Write your birthday here. _____

■ How old are you?_____ years _____ months

■ How old is Baby Joe?_____ months

■ How old is Baby Zoe?_____ months

■ How much older than that, in years, are you?_____ ✂

- -

| A season plate |

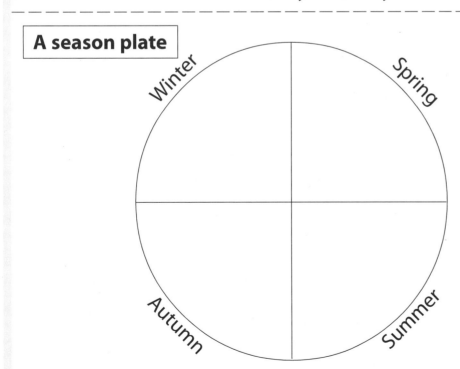

■ A year has four seasons. Draw a season picture in each quarter.

Ready to go! MATHS PUZZLES

Mental measure

A

How can you measure:

1. weight ———————————

2. liquid ————————————

3. your height —————————

4. the playground ————————

Name the measure for:

5. a ruler —————————————

6. a packet of sweets —————

7. a bottle of pop ——————————

8. a bag of potatoes ——————

9. a box of cereal———————————

10. petrol for a car————————

B

1. Add two to (5p) pieces ☐

2. Take 15p from 20p ☐

3. ☐ + ☐ = 10p

4. 10g – 9g = ☐

5. 50g + ☐ = 100g

6. 20cm – ☐ = 10cm

7. 100m – ☐ = 50m

8. 1 hr = ☐ mins

9. ½ hr = ☐ mins

10. ☐ hrs = 1 day

C

Read the problem. Use these words: More   Less   Same

1. 100cm and 1 metre ☐

2. 250g and 1 kilogram ☐

3. 1 litre and 1 cup ☐

4. 50 minutes and 1 hour ☐

5. £1 and 2 × 50p ☐

6. Your height is 120cm. How tall are you? ——— m ——— cm

7. A variety pack cereal weighs 250g. Write the sum to find the weight of an eight-pack.

8. Write the digital time for half past 10 in the morning ☐ half past 10 at night ☐

9. A Coke is 25p. How much is a four-pack? ☐

10. Estimate how many cups are in 1 litre. ☐

This section comprises 6 puzzle activities, 4 of which are accompanied by a photocopiable activity sheet for the children to complete. These activities are designed to familiarize children with concepts of classification and recording data which are essential to their future ability to understand and solve mathematical problems. All of the activities are focused on the Numeracy Strategy Framework's key objectives for organizing and using data in Years 1 and 2. These are as follows:

■ Organize and use data by sorting, classifying and organizing information in simple ways, for example pictures, lists of simple tables. Discuss the results.
■ Represent data as simple frequency tables, pictograms or block graphs and explain.
   The activities do not follow a particular sequence of skills so may be used at the teacher's discretion when these skills are being taught in the yearly programmes.

SORTING SETS

RESOURCES AND CLASSROOM ORGANIZATION
You will need a number of collections (preferably of real objects, rather than pictures), for example: things around the classroom (pens, pencils, paper, books, counters, counting blocks, beads); plastic models (zoo or farm animals, dinosaurs, vehicles, buildings, shapes). The children will work in small groups, depending on the materials you have provided for sorting.

WHAT TO DO
Start by asking: *How many children are in our class? How many boys? How many girls?* This is a simple example of sorting: all the children ➠ some boys and some girls. You could also try grouping by hair or eye colour. Then use a collection of objects to introduce the idea of sorting by criteria. For example, if pens, pencils and crayons were chosen from a collection of objects, you might say: *All these things can be used to write with, they are all writing materials.* You might then suggest: *Could we divide this group of writing materials into smaller groups – all the pens, for example?* Ask one child to collect this smaller group and show it to the class for them to check.

   Repeat this process with each sub-group of materials, emphasizing that the smaller group is still part of the bigger group. Once you are satisfied that the idea has been grasped, let the children work independently in as many groups as the materials for sorting allow. They should name the main group, then subdivide it into smaller groups. Each child should record the sorting on drawing paper independently, so that he or she can explain the criteria if asked. Finally, one person from each group can explain the sorting activity to the class.

DIFFERENTIATION
■ Mixed-ability grouping will provide the necessary support for sorting; but adult supervision of recording may be needed once the sorting is done.
■ Children should be encouraged to find other ways to sort (that is, different criteria) and list them.

NOW OR LATER
■ The children could search home shopping catalogues for a given type of item, cut out appropriate pictures and make a collage.

OBJECTIVE
To sort objects according to chosen criteria.

CROSS-CURRICULAR
SCIENCE
Sorting and classifying.

ENGLISH
Explaining thoughts clearly.

■ The children could put a variety of pictures into a large envelope to challenge each other on category recognition and sorting.

SNOWMAN

OBJECTIVES
■ To choose from given criteria.
■ To mix and match solutions.

CROSS-CURRICULAR
SCIENCE
Properties of materials.
DESIGN AND TECHNOLOGY
Choosing elements for a design.

RESOURCES AND CLASSROOM ORGANIZATION
Each child will need a copy of photocopiable page 60, a pencil, crayons and a blank sheet of paper. The photocopiable sheet may need to be cut into three (see below). You may wish to supply real items corresponding to the pictures in the top left-hand corner of the sheet.

WHAT TO DO
Start with a whole-class discussion on 'snowmen' and how to build them. Ask the children what items they would use to make the snowman look more human. If you have suitable items, show them to the children. What are the main types of items: hats, noses, eyes? Emphasize that designing a snowman is a matter of choice. Draw a large blank snowman (as on the photocopiable sheet) on the board or flip chart. Let the children choose one item from each of their categories for you to add. You may repeat this with different choices for comparison.

Give out copies of photocopiable page 60. Read out the instruction and refer to the examples you have just done. Explain that the eight snowmen should each have a different combination of items from the three boxes. When the children have completed the sheet, they may draw their favourite choice again on a separate sheet of paper (using crayons). These can be displayed, allowing the children to find out which is the most popular item in each category and which is the most popular composite choice. This should provide a lively concluding discussion.

DIFFERENTIATION
■ Some children may be overwhelmed by the full sheet of blank snowmen. They could be given only the top strip, then offered the remaining strips one at a time and helped with choices.
■ Providing further choices in each category, or in a new category, will extend the investigation. The same idea could be applied to the design of clown faces and costumes.

NOW OR LATER
■ The children could make a greeting card with a cut-out snowman (or clown).
■ Working in groups, they could make snow scenes with their favourite snowman designs cut out and stuck onto a background.
■ The children could make a storyboard sequence of instructions for building a snowman.

Holiday packing

Resources and classroom organization

Each child will need at least three copies of photocopiable page 61 (provided one at a time), a pencil and five coloured crayons: red, blue, green, yellow and black. The four clothing templates on the sheet could be photocopied onto card, cut out and traced, drawn around, or they could simply be copied into the spaces.

What to do

This investigation can be embarked upon with the minimum of instruction: the children can be given the activity sheet and left to work through the two-colour combinations. They could work either individually or in pairs for discussing and comparing. Encourage them to find **all** the possible two-colour combinations, remembering that each pair of colours is two possible outfits. Children working in pairs would have one child finding the combinations for a summer outfit (tee-shirts and shorts) and the other child exploring winter possibilities (sweaters and trousers). Their results can then be shared and discussed together. Each child will need at least one copy of the photocopiable sheet to explore all the possibilities. You could use an example of a two-colour choice for each outfit to help them get started.

Differentiation

■ To simplify the task, reduce the number of colours.
■ To extend the task, add white (or another colour) to the five choices.

Now or later

■ The children could plan their own mix-and-match holiday packing for summer or winter, limiting the range of colours or types of garmnent allowed.
■ They could design a mix-and-match line of tracksuits or football kits.

Objectives
■ To investigate combinations using two criteria.
■ To work systematically.

Cross-curricular
Science
Investigative reasoning.

PSHE
Making personal choices.

MOVING AROUND

OBJECTIVE
To use appropriate mathematical language for sorting sets.

CROSS-CURRICULAR
ENGLISH
Speaking and listening.

SCIENCE
Reasoning from facts.

RESOURCES AND CLASSROOM ORGANIZATION
Prepare a set of category cards and question cards as shown in Figure 1.

WHAT TO DO
Introduce the vocabulary that you wish to emphasize in this activity: words such as **group, set, count, sort** and **data.** Tell the children that they are going to work in groups to collect data.

Divide the class into small groups. Explain that this is a talking activity about how we get around, and that you will be asking them to report back to the class when they have had a chance to collect some data. Give each group one of the category cards and a large sheet of paper. Introduce each category by giving an example of a question to discuss, such as:

■ **Legs** – *How many different ways could you use your legs to move from place to place?*
■ **To school** – *How many different ways do you and the other children come to school?*
Allow enough discussion and recording time; then ask each of the groups in turn to come to the front, and call on one child from each group to use the chart to explain what they have discussed. Others in the group may add their comments. Ask the rest of the class for any further suggestions they can make. Help the children to put their reports into the language of data handling, using the words you reviewed at the beginning. You may need to do this by asking questions, such as: *How many children in your group can run? Is that a full* **set**? *How many of your group come to school by car? Can you* **sort** *them by type of car? What* **data** *are you giving me here?*

Conclude by summarizing what you have learned about the class from each group report.

DIFFERENTIATION
Carefully assigned mixed ability groupings will inevitably provide differentiation in these tasks. You will also find that some categories lend themselves to 'pictogram' recording techniques which would be suited to children with poorer writing skills.

NOW OR LATER
■ Give each child a sheet of paper folded into three columns with headings: either Wheels/Air/Water or To school/To town/To holiday. Ask them to collect data from the group charts.
■ Choose other situations to discuss and categorize, such as: With or without engines; Travelling to distant places; Slow or fast transport.
■ The children could do a vehicle survey outside (with adult supervision), sorting what they see by vehicle type and/or colour.

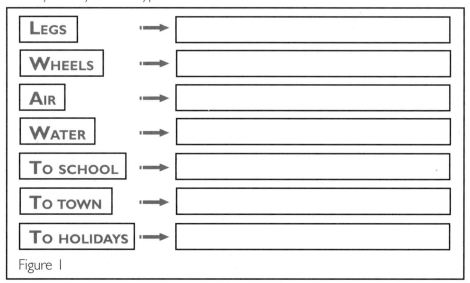

Figure 1

TRAY COLLECTIONS

RESOURCES AND CLASSROOM ORGANIZATION

You will need to prepare a tray with some familiar objects on it, such as: apple, toy, spoon, feather, ring, shell, plate, flower, ball, brooch, pebble, dice. Provide some tokens such as counters. Make one copy per child of photocopiable page 62.

WHAT TO DO

Divide the children into two teams. Explain that this is a **matching** game. A team wins a counter for every successful **object match** they can make from the tray.

The first child from each team should come forward to the tray, one of them will choose an object and say something about it. Then the child from the other team has to choose something from the tray which will match the first object in some way. The child has to justify the match – for example, 'apple goes with ball because they have the same shape'. Having earned a token for the team by making a successful match, this child then chooses another object for the first child to match so that each has a chance to earn a token. Chosen objects are replaced on the tray for the next two children to challenge one another.

Award a point for each match that is justified by a good explanation. Encourage the children to identify properties such as colour, use, texture, materials and cost. Every child will have a turn. Allow those who need most help to watch initially and have a turn later. As the game progresses, reasons for matching items may be repeated; but as this is reinforcing for less confident children, points may still be awarded. Each team's tokens can be added up at the end of the game to find the winning team – but usually it will end in a draw!

Finally, give each child a copy of photocopiable page 62. Explain that the children have to draw two matching objects in each of

the tray shapes, then write underneath each tray how the match works. You may prefer to remove the tray from sight while the children do this, so that they have to use their memory.

DIFFERENTIATION

■ Less confident children could take their turns later in the game (see above). You may prefer to leave the tray and objects in view while the children are working on the photocopiable sheet.
■ Ask more confident children to add one or more new objects to each tray, matching objects already there and stating their criteria for matching.

NOW OR LATER

■ Play a version of 'Kim's Game': cover the tray with a cloth, remove one object, then reveal the tray and ask the children what is missing.
■ The children could work in pairs to devise a matching pairs domino game.
■ Try playing oral memory games involving lists that grow (such as 'My aunt went to market and bought...') with the children.

MAKING GRAPHS

OBJECTIVE

To collect data and record it:
■ using tally marks;
■ using a block graph.

RESOURCES AND CLASSROOM ORGANIZATION

Collect empty crisp packets in five different flavours. The children will need squared paper, rulers and coloured pencils.

WHAT TO DO

Introduce the children to the idea of collecting data with a simple example: *I am going to ask each of you about a favourite snack. I've chosen crisps with these different flavours to choose from.* Display your prepared set of five crisp packets with different flavours. List the flavours on the board or flip chart.

Go round the class, asking each child to choose their favourite flavour. Draw a tally mark next to each choice on the board or flip chart. Once the survey is complete, show the children how to count up the tally marks. Say that this data can also be shown as a **block graph**. Point to the information you have: the list of flavours and the tally marks. Draw the horizontal axis and label it with the five crisp flavours; then draw the vertical axis and label it with numbers, starting at 0 where the two lines meet. (See Figure 2.)

Point to the vertical axis and say: *This line will show us how many children chose each flavour.* Ask the children to look at the counted tally marks and tell you how many of them preferred the first flavour on the list. Ask a volunteer to show you this number on the vertical line and the flavour on the bottom line, then mark the diagram at the correct point above the bottom line. You can then draw a 'block' up to the mark. Record the rest of the data in this way. When the block graph is complete, ask the children to suggest questions to ask each other about what they can see.

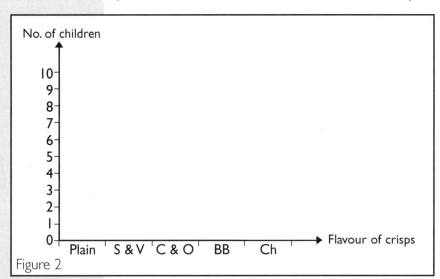

Figure 2

Finally, give each child a sheet of squared paper. Tell the children that you want them to draw the same block graph that you have shown them then make up some questions about it.

This activity can be repeated many times, using other sets of choices such as favourite colours, breakfast cereals, TV programmes, toys or games. In each case, the maximum number of choices should be six. The axis line data can also be reversed.

DIFFERENTIATION

■ Some children may need to draw the correct number of stick people above each choice instead of using the block format, to clarify the representation.
■ Other children may be able to collect their own data (based on your suggestions), draw a block graph and use it to describe their findings to the rest of the class.

NOW OR LATER

■ Find some other kinds of graphs and see whether the children can read information from them.
■ Talk about temperature line graphs: what they look like and what they tell you.
■ Make a class graph of attendance over 2 weeks. Talk about what it shows.
■ Keep a class weather chart for a month, then record the overall findings as a block graph.

CAR PARKING – COLOUR SORT

RESOURCES AND CLASSROOM ORGANIZATION

You will need four model cars – black, red, blue and yellow – for demonstration. Each child will need a copy of photocopiable page 63 and four coloured pencils (see cars).

WHAT TO DO

Use the model cars to demonstrate the idea of the investigation. Explain: *Every day, four people who work in the same office park their cars in the same strip of the company's car park. The boss always takes the first space with a black car, but the other employees often change their spaces. Your job is to see how many different ways they can park.* Let's do one together to start you off. Demonstrate a sequence (such as black, red, blue, yellow) by placing the cars on a sheet marked with four spaces, starting with the black car.

Give each child a copy of the photocopiable sheet, and let the children copy this initial sequence at the top of the sheet. Now let them make another sequence in each of the 'Try' boxes. Remind them to place the black car in the first space each time.

Conclude by discussing the children's answers and how they solved the problem. They should have found all of the possible arrangements (there are six). Note whether they worked systematically through the options or swapped at random.

DIFFERENTIATION

■ Some children may need to carry on moving the model cars with adult supervision, copying each new sequence one at a time.
■ The reasoning involved in this investigation can be extended by suggesting: *Suppose the boss decides to keep her car in one of the two middle spaces. Will this change the number of possible arrangements for the other cars?*

NOW OR LATER

■ The children could use car brochures to compile a list of car makes and ask each child in the class to choose one. They could then determine favourite choices.
■ A survey of the children's favourite car colours could be made and discussed.
■ Working with adult supervision, the children could make a survey of the car colours in a car park.

OBJECTIVE
To develop reasoning strategies.

**CROSS CURRICULAR
SCIENCE**
Logical investigation.

Name   Date

Snowman investigation

■ Use these items to decorate the snowmen. Choose only one item from each box for each snowman.

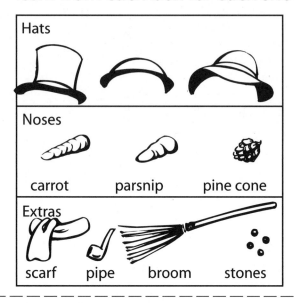

Hats

Noses

carrot   parsnip   pine cone

Extras

scarf   pipe   broom   stones

Name _____ Date _____

Holiday packing

You will need red, blue, green, yellow and black crayons.

■ Choose a summer or a winter outfit.

■ Draw the clothes in the boxes below. Colour them in with your crayons. Make your outfits different colours in as many ways as you can. Try one here:

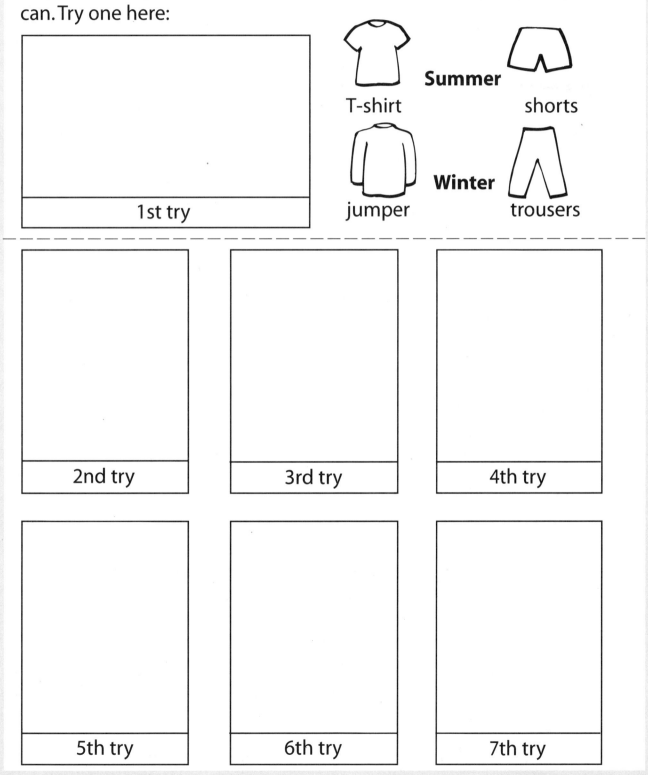

| 1st try |

Summer

T-shirt   shorts

Winter

jumper   trousers

| 2nd try | 3rd try | 4th try |

| 5th try | 6th try | 7th try |

Tray collections

■ Put **two** matching objects on each tray.

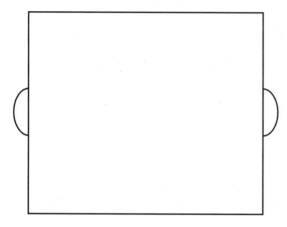

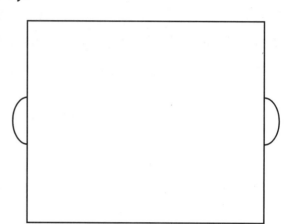

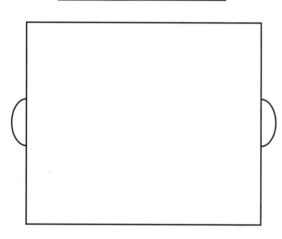

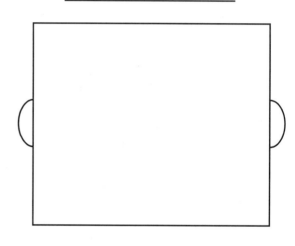

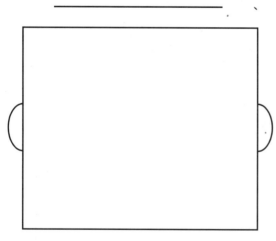

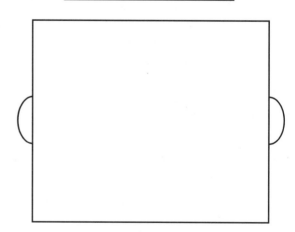

■ Write **colour, shape, use** or **feel** to explain each match.

Car parking

Every day the
black car parks
here. ——————▶

A red car, a blue car and a yellow car park in the other spaces.
■ See how many different ways you can park them. Put the black
car in first.

1st try ——————▶

2nd try ——————▶

3rd try ——————▶

4th try ——————▶

5th try ——————▶

NATIONAL STANDARDS FOR KEY SKILLS

All of the puzzle activities in this book are designed to fit within four themes that are appropriate to children at this age level:

- Myself and my world (**My**);
- Out and about (**O & A**);
- Fun and games (**F & G**);
- Times and seasons (**S**).

Title	Theme	Skills
Section 1		
Fingerplay	My	Counting 1–10
Number lines	F & G	Counting 1–10
Where do you live?	My	Number sequences
Tallying with 5s and 10s	My	Counting 1–10
Skittle scores	F & G	Number bonds to 10
Pinball wizard	F & G	Addition and subtraction to 20
Function machines investigation	F & G	Number bonds to 20
Caterpillar counting	F & G	Number sequences
Multi-storey flats	O & A	Number sequences
Darts	F & G	Number bonds to 20 / Counting in 10s
Going mental? No problem!	F & G	Number vocabulary and problem solving
100 square gameboards	F & G	Counting forward and backwards
Section 2		
Shapes everywhere	O & A	Exploring properties of 4 basic shapes
Shape pictures	O & A	Exploring properties of 4 basic shapes
Picasso patterns	F & G	Exploring properties of 4 basic shapes
Shape codes	F & G	Exploring properties of 4 basic shapes
Under the pyramids	O & A	Following directions
Walk this way	O & A	Following directions
Compass points	O & A	Describing position / Following directions
Pie and pizza	My	Dividing regular shapes
Through the looking glass	F & G	Pattern and symmetry
Squared paper symmetry	F & G	Pattern and symmetry
Discovering tessellating patterns	F & G	Pattern and symmetry
Squaring the square	F&G	Shape construction
An Easter egg tangram	S	Shape construction
Section 3		
Portable measures	My	Exploring length
Just my size!	My	Exploring length
Classroom measure	My	Exploring length
Breakfast cereals	My	Exploring capacity and mass
Tea and biscuits	My	Exploring capacity and mass
Change machines	My	Money manipulation
Jelly bean mixture	My	Sorting mass
Timespan	S	Developing time sense
How long does it take?	S	Developing time sense
Mental measure	My	Measure vocabulary and estimating
Section 4		
Sorting sets	My	Sorting and counting
Snowman	S	Exploring criteria for sorts
Holiday packing	S	Exploring criteria for sorts
Moving around	O & A	Sorting by given criteria
Tray collections	F & G	Memory sorting
Making graphs	My	Data representation
Car parking colour sort	O & A	Reasoning strategies